I

14
2

p2

WD

THE NELSONIAN LIBRARY

EDITED BY JOHN HAMPDEN

"LET'S GO RIDING!"

No. 45

"LET'S GO RIDING!"

by

B. L. KEARLEY

Illustrated by
Colin Dilly

THOMAS NELSON & SONS LTD
LONDON EDINBURGH PARIS MELBOURNE
TORONTO AND NEW YORK

First Published, 1937

TO
LIGHTNING
WHOSE TALE MAY ONE DAY BE TOLD

CONTENTS

FULL-PAGE ILLUSTRATIONS

" Is Mr. Wisp about, please ? " asked John of a short, rather stout, aged man, with a very brown face, and little black eyes, which twinkled somehow in spite of their cunning.

" I'll see, si-." Touching his forelock, he disappeared towards the notice " Office."

" I suppose that's a groom ? " said Jane.

" 'Spect so," said John; " weird-looking bird. Hope Mr. Wisp hasn't forgotten our appointment."

" Uncle Fred said he was a good scout. Here he comes. Good-afternoon, Mr. Wisp."

" Good-afternoon, Miss Jane. Good-afternoon, Master John. Glad to see you're nicely on time, as the monkey said when he sat on the clock. How do the clothes feel ? "

" Fine, thank you ; only the jodhpurs were a bit tight to get over the ankle. Weren't they, Jane ? "

" Yes, they were. In fact mine feel tight now."

" So they should," said Mr. Wisp; " if they were at all loose they'd soon ruck and be very uncomfortable on the saddle. When you've worn a pair of jodhpurs a few times it's a good idea to have a strap, about two inches wide, round the leg just below the knee. It prevents them turning round. I'll get them for you from my saddler when you need them.

" Now, what about a look round the stables before we start ? I know you're in a hurry to get on the horses, but it's just as well to have a look round first. We've got the afternoon before us."

They followed his tall, spare figure, wearing a

deep brown long-skirted coat (slightly darned and with a leather binding to the cuffs), bowler hat, fawn breeches, and black soft leather boots.

There were neat green buckets of water outside the doors, initialled W. W., a red crunchy sand on the cobbles ; the doors were green and the threshold stones snow white.

" Looks very clean and nice, doesn't it ? " said Jane.

" Yes," said John, and, *sotto voce*, " I like his breeches and boots."

" So do I. Awfully smart. But they cost more than jodhpurs, and you, at any rate, would grow out of them too soon."

" And I don't suppose you've stopped growing yet, big sister, despite your great age," put in John.

" Well, perhaps not," laughed sixteen-year-old Jane ; " but anyhow Dad says our outfits cost enough as it is."

Mr. Wisp unlatched the door and ushered them in. " The first thing to remember in a stable," he said, " is to pick your feet up. Any stableman knows a horseman by the way he walks over the straw— drag your feet and the straw drags with you. The next thing is, always speak to a horse as you approach him—' Whey, old fellow.' They are still animals after all, and their natural impulse is to kick when startled from behind. Now this is Black Prince— you'll ride him some day, John."

" He *is* black. Shall I ride him too ? " asked Jane.

" I expect so, but I've one or two better suited

3

to a young woman. By the way, John, have you ever seen a horse with his head where his tail ought to be ? No ? Well, here's one—Mary—the pony your sister is going to ride to-day."

" But she's only turned round this way ready to go out."

" That's just it, young fellow—her head ought to be in the manger. These reins from the stall posts to her bit are called pillar reins ; see, this one is wrong, it should pass *under* the bridle rein, not over it. If ever you have stablemen of your own, John, you will find that however they work, however reliable, you'll always need a sharp eye. Old Bob,

4

the man you saw as you came in the yard, is a wonderful groom and a rare old character; he'll be spinning you some yarns one day before long, and if he likes you, Jane, you'll be 'Milady,' and you John, will be 'Captain,' or 'Milord.' That little joke about the horse's head being where his tail ought to be is one of his favourites, and he loves to have a little bet on with any one who shows off or swanks.

"In this riding business we get people of all descriptions. Some ride naturally, some are good, some nervous, some will never be any good; we have to deal with them all, but the ones we dislike are those who won't be taught. After a few lessons they think they know it all, and buy spurs with chains on; slap their boots with long whips, and boast to their friends of this and that horse they rode, and are always asking for what they call a 'better' horse. It would be dangerous to put them on anything but the quietest, or 'patent safety,' as they're called.

"We had one young fellow the other day who said he wouldn't ride Connie any more—if he couldn't have another he'd go somewhere else. Now Connie is a mare you'll love. She has the quietest and sweetest of temperaments, and is nearly the only horse we could put this young man on with safety. So I sent Old Bob on to the common to mount him, knowing that although he took Connie he'd persuade him to get on her. How did he do it? Simply gave her another name, called her Sally, and said

I'd just bought her ! When the young man came in after his ride he said, ' That's more like the horse for me—don't send anything else again.'

" He didn't know one horse from another, and you can just imagine the contempt we get for people like that ; and ladies are often as bad. You will find that the finest horsemen, and women, are not only the kindest of people, but they are also the most modest. That's a lesson I shall often be teaching you. The finer the horseman the quieter he is, because he finds the more he knows the more he has to learn. Of course that sounds like a paradox, but as you get on you'll see what I mean. Anyway, I bet you'll be cheeky enough by the time you've jumped a few fences."

" How long will it be before we can jump ? It looks easy enough."

" So it does. Depends how quickly you learn, but nothing is gained by trying to go too fast. When you do start to jump, you'll find there's nothing like it."

" Doris Fitzsimmons—she's at my school, you know, and about three forms lower—says she's been jumping a long time, and last Christmas hols she had two days' hunting."

" Oh well, if she's like her twin brother, who's in our form, she'll always be bragging about something," said John.

" It's quite impressive all the same. What a lovely soft nose Mary has. She fairly snuggles up. Does she like sugar, Mr. Wisp ? "

" You try her. But don't give her too much. It's better to reward a horse after your ride. . . . Sugar makes them foam at the mouth."

" Is that a good or a bad thing ? "

" Well, John, it's good in this way. If a horse is inclined to have a dry mouth and is also strong willed, he can get a firm, fixed hold on the bit which enables him to get out of the rider's control and run away. When that happens the strongest man can do nothing except keep cool if there's plenty of free space for the horse to gallop until tired, or get off him. Of course not many horses are like that, and you may never get on one. Sugar makes the bit slip easily, so that a rider can move the bit in his horse's mouth, and keep his head flexible. Other horses toss their heads a lot, and then you get covered in sticky wet foam, which is difficult to clean off your clothes."

" Any chance of Mary tossing about ? "

" No ; but if you do get any on you, the only thing to use is a sponge and cold water."

" Thanks, I'll remember that. I say, John, what horse are you going to ride ? "

" I don't know yet. Where is he, Mr. Wisp ? I'm anxious to see my fiery steed."

" In the next stall but one. This one here is Bob, the cob. A good, useful horse to me. Never takes too much out of himself or the rider ; he's a knowing card. He can sum up any one immediately they get on him. For some he will only just trot, and he knows the very second it's time to come home.

Nobody can get him to stay out longer than he should. One day a customer took him out, and I met Bob on his way home, travelling quite gently, with an empty saddle. I found the young man later, and he told me that *he* wanted to go one way and Bob wanted to go another, so he turned the horse round and round to make him giddy, but he got giddy first and fell off! Now here's your horse for to-day—a brown mare, Polly. Are the pillar reins right this time ? "

" Yes, I think so."

" And you, Jane ? "

" Yes, I'm *sure*."

" Good. Well, there's my horse in the next stall. His name is Cocktail ; a nice colour, grey—but not the best of shapes. The man I bought him from called him Cocktail because he said he was the prelude to better things. Don't suppose you drink cocktails yet ? "

" No," replied Jane, " but I had a sip of Uncle Fred's one day. Overrated taste, I thought."

" Dad says they're slow poison," put in John.

" Well, Cocktail's a good horse anyway. As good as a nurse."

Old Bob, the groom, had been following them quietly for the last few minutes, although only Mr. Wisp noticed him.

" Right, Bob," said the riding master, " that's enough for now. Bring them out."

" Yessir."

Mr. Wisp opened the stable door.

CHAPTER TWO

THE yard made a lovely picture as Mary, Polly, and the grey Cocktail were led out. The September sun was still warm, and lighted the thatched roofs and red bricks with a mellow glow, making the liver chestnut of Mary gleam almost blue. Jane was all excited inside, and John stood trying not to look anxious. This was LIFE!

Old Bob brought Mary forward to the centre, whilst a most picturesque, villainous-looking man held Polly and Cocktail. He was about six feet two inches tall, wearing an old felt hat and brown shoes, and dressed in a shiny blue suit. He had a white " stock " round his neck, tied with rather a flare, fastened horizontally by a gold hunting-horn. He was very lean, and his face was brown, seamed with long furrows down either cheek ; he seemed to be chewing something ; his eyes were rather prominent with a bird-like expression, missing nothing.

Jane had an uncomfortable feeling when she first looked at him, thinking that he might easily be a pirate in modern clothes, but at her second look she noticed a certain wistfulness of the mouth, and when he caught her eyes a most charming smile

9

removed all trace of villainy. He lifted his hat with, " How would you be now, Missy ? " in a soft Irish brogue.

Her mind was brought back by Mr. Wisp talking to John.

" Stand just over here. Never get near a horse's heels. Always stand forward. He can kick behind, but not in front.

" Now, Jane. Before you can ride a horse you've got to mount it. Stand on the left side ; no, here by the shoulder with your back to the horse's head. Right. Place the reins in your left hand and put it on the withers in front of the saddle ; don't take the reins up too short or your horse may run back or rear—just take a length like this—see—one that is neither too tight nor too loose. Now take hold of the stirrup with the right hand, thumb in towards you, and lift your left foot—place it in the stirrup up to the instep, and then take hold of the waist of the saddle with your right hand. Now spring from the right foot, bring both feet together—move your right hand from the back to the front of the saddle and lift your right leg over, and sit down *gently*.

" Good, not so bad—and now dismount and try once more.

" No, don't hurry to get down—always be gentle with horses. Lift your right leg back over to the left foot ; standing in the stirrup, take hold of the back of the saddle with the right hand, and the front with the left ; now, supporting yourself on your hands, take the feet out of the stirrup. Keep both feet

THEY'RE OFF!

BACK TO HORSE'S HEAD   FOOT IN IRON

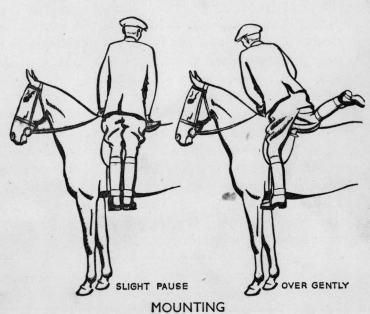

SLIGHT PAUSE   OVER GENTLY

MOUNTING

together and gently drop ; that's fine, as agile as an antelope !

" Up once more—reins first and hand on withers, back to horse's head, left foot in stirrup, right hand on saddle, spring, feet together, over. See that, John ?

" Now for the length of stirrup. Take your foot out and let the leg drop naturally. If the stirrup bottom strikes just below the ankle bone it's the right length. It does. Now, John, your turn to mount Polly. That's good. Always remember to mount with your back to the horse's head, because even if he starts off before you are quite ready he won't leave you behind. I've seen people sit down suddenly for doing it wrongly."

They both watched the quiet skilful way in which Mr. Wisp mounted Cocktail. Jane was placed on his near side, and John on the off. Jane wondered how he could tell which rein was which, as he had leading reins to manage as well as his own, and to her they seemed a bunch.

They rode out of the yard, and in a few minutes were on the common. The earth was springy beneath the horses' feet, and smelt slightly damp as the leaves were fast turning on the trees. High above them a kite flew in the breeze, its distant string connected to a young enthusiast.

To Jane and John the horses beneath them felt wide, and the movement strange—not a bit like the donkeys they had occasionally ridden during seaside holidays. Jane said so to John, who replied, " Oh, well, we were only kids then," and before they had time to generalize further Mr. Wisp was off again.

"Now I want you both to remember that when you're on a horse the way you sit and hold yourself is very important. It makes or mars your riding. Your back should be straight and shoulders square. Your head should be up and looking well to the front. The arms should be upright from the shoulder to the elbow, the elbows close to the sides, with the hands low; that's right, Jane. Now both look down and tell me how much of your feet you can see. You, John?"

SEE ⅔ OF FOOT

"My toes."

"Jane?"

"Nothing."

"Well, both look again—no, don't lean forward to do it— glance down from the upright position, and push your legs forward until you can see from your toe to the instep where I placed the stirrup. Good, that means that your leg from the knee downwards is upright, and parallel with your arm from the shoulder to the elbow. If your legs remain like that, you will get the correct position in the saddle, and never be taken unawares by your horse should he shy or buck. Now put your feet level, and turn them nearly parallel to the horse; that's right, my lad."

13

" Why do the feet have to be nearly parallel to the horse, Mr. Wisp ? " asked John.

" Because only then can your knees fit close to the saddle. Turn them out and see how your knees come away. Although a lot of riding is balance you *must* grip with your knees. When a man rides well we say he has a ' good seat.' By this we mean that he sits firmly, lightly, and flexibly in his saddle. Every one at first is inclined to be a bit stiff, but that doesn't matter if they sit up well and square. Riding in cars and buses makes people round-shouldered. You sit as I tell you, and you'll find the flexibility comes in time.

" John, you're sitting too far back—move forward a little and sit in the well of the saddle. Jane, just hollow your back a little more between the shoulders. . . . Have you any idea what bridles you're using ? "

" Not the faintest."

" A bridle is the most important part of a horse's tackle ; it's important to him as well as to you. In time I shall teach you something about bitting, but to-day you're using single-rein plain-ring snaffles —the snaffle, of course, being the bit, which is the kindest one can use."

" Why is that ? " said Jane. " I thought a bit was just a bit."

" A lot of people think so, but, forgive the pun, not a bit of it. Horses' mouths vary considerably, and it takes an expert to suit them properly. A snaffle is a simple bit and doesn't pinch at all, and

14

can't hurt even when people are learning and apt to help their balance by hanging on the reins, and so on the horse's mouth. These have single reins because I don't want to confuse you at the outset. You've been holding them anyhow so far, but if you watch me I'll show you how they should be held.

" Take a rein in each hand, placing it between the little finger and the third finger ; the hand over the top of the rein, not under it ; run the rein

RELAXED   CONTROLLED

HOLDING REINS

through the hand, clasping it with three fingers and catching it between the thumb and first finger, and let the loop hang on the right hand side. Don't turn your knuckles to the sky ; let the backs of your hands be parallel to the slope of the horse's shoulder. If your hands are turned over too much, you will pull from the biceps and chest. Keep them like this, and the pull will come from the shoulders through the arms.

" Now when I say, ' Shorten your rein,' I mean that your reins are too slack, so you do it like this, one hand at a time. Loosen the hold slightly, catch the rein behind the thumb with one hand and slide the other forward a few inches ; then do the same to the other hand. It's an important movement, and soon becomes easy. When I say, ' Ease your rein,' lower the hands and slide them back a few inches. The length of rein should be sufficient to keep a gentle contact with the horse's mouth ; when we trot and canter the rein will need to be shorter, but we shan't bother with more than walking to-day. Turn your wrists over and outward, and keep your hands down ; although you are sitting upright, let your wrists, hands, and arms be responsive to your horse. Give when he gives, and take when he takes.

" It's rather early yet to talk about ' good hands,' although if I can only help you to acquire them it will make you enjoy riding more, not to mention how much your horses will appreciate them, Jane."

" I've heard the term ' good hands,' and often wondered what it meant," said Jane. " I suppose it really means a sympathetic contact with a horse's mouth ? "

" Ah, and not only that. It means perfect grip and balance in horse and rider."

Cocktail was rather a fast walker, and every now and then Mary or Polly would give a few jog-trot paces to keep up. Mr. Wisp could see that his pupils would ride passably before long, and noted with satisfaction how keen they were. Quietly he reminded them to look at their feet, to sit up, to keep the hands low, move the hands, to "shorten the reins," stressing the importance of keeping an even but light feel of the horse's mouth and letting the hands move freely.

He was the epitome of patience and sympathy. His varied and wide experience of all types of people, of all ages, and their reaction to his teaching made him wary of overdoing instruction at first. He preferred questions to be answered when asked, and never tired of explaining the most trivial details. It was his job and he loved it. He cared not whether a man were lord or commoner ; if he liked horses and he rode, if he liked them and didn't ride, it was all one.

With the passing of the years he had adapted himself to changing conditions ; sensible enough to appreciate the advantages of motors whilst deploring their lack of romance; their " futile utility " was his pet description. He had seen a good deal of sport in his day, and was considered a first-rate man to hounds. He no longer jumped the places he had but on the dozen or so days he now stole in a season he could be seen quietly keeping within striking distance of hounds, and was an excellent pilot for any pupil, being patient and sympathetic with the nervous, and mildly restraining to the impetuous.

To the casual observer he appeared a man without ambition ; perhaps he was in a worldly sense, but horses were the very fibre of his being, and he found much happiness with them in a somewhat lonely life. He had to earn his daily bread, and to use his own words, " I'd rather earn good-tasting bread than bad-tasting caviare."

His success in teaching was due to ability to inspire confidence, not only in those he taught but in the animals that carried them. He was quickly on good terms with any horse he rode, and in his younger days people marvelled at the way every horse jumped, and the ease with which they appeared to carry him. Horses known to be sticky or sluggish ; cunning horses and those supposed to run away were often lent, and sometimes sold to him. He attributed this ability of getting any horse to go well to establishing the horse's confidence in himself and assuming right away that they would get on well together. There is nothing to which a horse will respond so quickly.

John and Jane were both keen and intelligent, and although their father was not rich he was able and willing to develop their riding in a moderate manner, knowing full well that the benefit to their health, and the character thus moulded, would amply repay him.

CHAPTER THREE

TIME FLIES

THEY were now on the regular sandy track, where a few people were also riding. Some learning, like themselves, and one or two, bold but obviously amateur spirits, cantered alone, envied by John until Mr. Wisp said, " We haven't seen a good rider yet; these are some of the people I told you about—they need taking in hand if only they'd allow it. That young woman on the skewbald isn't too bad if only she'd keep her hands down and sit up better. How are *you* sitting, Jane ? "

" Well, I can see three parts of my feet. By the way, what's a skewbald, Mr. Wisp ? "

" A skewbald is a bay and white, chestnut and white, or brown and white horse. It comes in the 'odd coloured' class, as we call them. Piebald's another ; that's black and white."

" I always cross the toes of my shoes with a finger when I see a piebald—for luck, you know."

" And does it bring it ? "

"Not so that you'd notice," broke in John; "and it's a kid's trick, anyway."

" Sometimes it's quite effective, John. Don't you remember how badly we wanted to see the circus two Christmases ago, and then, just after you'd

19

It depends a lot on their breeding and whether they are what is called an early or late foal."

" What's that ? "

" An early foal is one born in March, when the weather is perhaps still cold, and a late one is born in July in hot weather, and the time to change coat will be governed by birth all their life. The usual time for foals is April and May. So early foals need clipping earlier."

" I love them when they're young, they look so sweet. There was one on the farm where we stayed once."

" That was only a farm horse," said John.

" Anyway, it was a foal—and a darling."

" Quite right, Jane. Farm horses shouldn't be despised. They are also becoming scarce, and do jolly useful and honest work."

" Are they clipped ? "

" No, their natural coat is left to protect them. Some people think no horses should be clipped ; but if you don't clip riding horses, especially hunters, they get so hot galloping that it reduces their powers of endurance and takes too much out of them. A horse is very susceptible to change of temperature, and when he's been galloped with a heavy coat on he gets wet, wringing wet, and if brought into a stable may not dry until next morning. The only thing to do then is to rug him up at once and keep him warm. Horses soon catch cold.

" Cleaning is also most important, and it's far easier to get dirt out properly if the coat is clipped.

Every one who rides should know something about grooming a horse ; not necessarily because they ought to do it, but if they are taught they know how it should be done. It's one of the things I shall teach you."

" That'll be interesting. When do we start ? "

" Not yet. We mustn't go too fast or you'll be cutting school and popping into the stables."

" That's a good idea ! "

" Maybe, but not for you. I don't want Mr. Vanster appearing in his wrath ; that would stop all the fun we're going to have. There's a paddock at the back of the stables where we shall teach you to jump, and put you through your paces bare back. You mustn't think because we only walk to-day that I'm a slow old coach. I want you to get used to your horses, and to become at home with everything connected with them. If you get on well there are lots of things we can do. I'll take you to the point-to-point races, and next summer go to a horse show. We might go to a gymkhana or two where you can enter—that's mounted sports, you know, musical chairs, relay races, obstacle races, and what not."

" That sounds topping. Is it all mounted ? "

" Oh yes, they're great fun. Mary's very handy for them, and Polly won the musical chairs at the last we went to."

" Good for her. What sort of prizes are there ? "

" Cups, tankards, whips, silver spoons, sometimes money."

" Sounds all right, doesn't it, John ? "

" Rather; I'm all for it."

" Well, just speak to your horses, and tell 'em. Jane, pat Mary on the neck and say ' Good old girl,' and you do the same, John. Never be self-conscious or afraid to speak to your horse. They like to hear your voice. Watch me speak to Cocktail :

" ' Cocktail, old boy, there's a good fellow.'

" There, see his ear come back to listen ? Always speak quietly and gently, and pat them now and again. A happy horse makes a happy rider.

" I had a young woman come to learn last summer and she could *not* speak to her horse. She thought it silly, and yet she'd kiss and cuddle her dog ! She hadn't much sympathy with horses really. I had to tell her so at last, and she became offended and never came back. She annoyed me too. She had a poor little light hunting-crop, with no thong ; in fact it wasn't strong enough to carry a thong, but she would insist on bringing it. It was no good as a whip, and, in any case, she couldn't manage her reins with or without it. An onlooker would have thought I didn't know my job to allow her to carry such a thing, but she fancied herself with it, and *would* have it. I was glad when she went. . . . We shall have to turn for home now. Do you feel more comfortable and easy in the saddle, Jane ? John, you're still a little too far back."

" Yes, thanks. I'm more comfortable," said Jane; " in fact I've become quite acclimatized. Feel as though I'd ridden all my life. I'm longing

24

to hear what you're going to tell us about the different colours of horses."

" Oh yes, and you shall count them. Remember how to tell a horse's colour ? "

" Yes, by the muzzle."

" Good ; that's the main colour. I'll tell you as we go. You will think some of them funny, and if you remember to ask me again some day I expect I shall be able to point out one or two you didn't know, as a lot of people ride round here.

" The simple ones first. Black, brown. It's difficult sometimes to tell a black from a dark brown. Polly is brown, John. Light bay, is light red-brown with dark points. The points are the ears, mane, legs, and tail. Dark bay is a dark reddish brown with dark, nearly black, points. Mealy bay you rarely see ; it's a light mealy brown, usually with a white leg or two. Golden or bright chestnut. Liver chestnut, like Mary, Jane, and mealy chestnut, which is like mealy bay, only it has a silver mane and tail. Piebald, black and white. Skewbald, chestnut or bay and white. Dun. A dun is a lovely colour, rather uncommon as he is nearly yellow with dark points and a dark line down the centre of his back to his tail. The line down the back is called a list. It is believed that wild horses, years and years ago, were mainly dun, and some people think that a dun, as he throws back to the original horse, is weaker than some colours, but my own experience is that a dun is usually a very sporty, game, and well-constitutioned horse. How many is that ? "

"Eleven," said Jane, who was keeping full count on her fingers.

"The colours of a horse are either pigmental or structural. You know that paints are pigments, or dyes. So the colour of a black horse is due to black melanin in the skin, and chestnut to red pigment, and these two pigments are mixed in varying proportions in bay and brown horses. But the white hair of a white horse is a structural colour, similar to white clouds. And that brings us to greys.

"For some reason no one ever calls a horse white. He is always called a grey or a light grey, although as he grows old he becomes practically white. Anyhow, we'll count that as one, light grey. Then there is dapple grey; he is a dark blue-grey with darker patches on his body, as if he'd stood under the trees a long time on hot sunny days and gone lighter where the sun has come through the leaves. Iron-grey is a dark bluey-grey all over, with dark points. Flea-bitten grey is a light grey flecked all over, rather like ermine, only ginger and not tufted. Then there's red roan, strawberry roan, and blue roan; all of which I shall have to point out to you when we see them.

"I'll show you a strawberry roan when we get back, as I've got one. He has a bad habit of rearing through having been badly broken, but is now only five years old, so I think we shall cure him. He's worth trying as he's well bred, and very affectionate. Rather like a new boy at school, John, who's not a bad sort of chap, but a bit ' uppish.' Would you like to see him ? "

" Please. Any chance of riding him ? "

" One day, perhaps. I expect a friend, who will be riding him for me next week, will be there when we get back. Now how many colours were there, Jane ? "

" Eighteen."

" Do you agree, John ? "

" I lost count when you were talking about the greys."

" Never mind, you can't remember them all at once ; but the main and most usual colours in this country are chestnut, bay, brown, grey, and black. Chestnuts usually have hot temperaments, whilst bays, browns, and greys are generally hard workers. . . . We shall be home in ten minutes."

" Heavens, how the time has gone."

" Thanks for the compliment. My star pupil is a young fellow named Peter who thinks I always try to cut his ride short. Came to me one day and asked if he could have a horse with a long neck because Irish Jack had told him ' the longer the rein the longer the ride,' whereas Jack really meant ' the longer the rein the *better* the ride.' That means, and it's quite true, especially of hunters, that the longer the neck and the better the front of a horse the more comfortable ride he is."

" How old is Peter, and does he ride well ? " asked John, who wondered if he were going to meet a boy of his own age.

" Oh, he's five or six years younger than you

27

are," replied Mr. Wisp. "He's a man of nine. He rides very well, as to the manner born. I expect he'll come out with us one day. You'll like him. He doesn't know the meaning of fear, and is quite a help to us in the stables. One day a pony trod on his foot and there they stood, the pony ignorant of the pain he was causing and Peter waiting for help. When old Bob noticed the trouble and moved the pony, Peter was rather white, as you can imagine, but all he said was, 'Drat the pony; but I s'pose if my feet were bigger he'd see them.' He's good at poetry too, and the first thing he'll ask you is if you know your ' piece,' as he calls it."

"Whatever is that ? "

"A little rhyme you ought to know. In fact I want you to remember it, *and* to practise it.

> Your head and your heart keep up,
> Your hands and your heels keep down,
> Your knees close in to your horse's sides,
> Your elbows close to your own.

Quite easy. The principles of riding. I'll repeat it. . . . If you put that into practice, you'll soon get on well. Can you remember it ? "

"Well," said John, " I'd rather learn that than Shakespeare. What do you say, Jane ? "

"Rather. I wish we were coming to-morrow."

"Good," said Mr. Wisp. "I can see we are going to like each other. Here we are back home again, all safe, sound, and bewildered with knowledge."

CHAPTER FOUR

GRAND CHAPS

AS they entered the yard the grooms bustled forward to the horses' heads.

"Pull your horses to a standstill gently, and speak to them quietly. Whoa, Cocktail. . . .

"Before you get off I want you to do an exercise, which we shall do later on the move. Drop your reins. Lift your right arm straight above your head; grip with your knees; keep your legs upright; now in a sweep bring your hand over and touch your left toe; now sit upright and drop the hands to the rein position. Good. Now the left hand. Up, down to the right toe, upright. Now do it two or three times, neatly, neatly. Right, that'll do.

"Now press your knees tight, and lean right back until your head rests on the horse's rump. . . . Three times more. Good, that'll develop your grip, and teach you not to hang on the reins. Now dismount. Don't hurry; do it methodically as I told you. Ease your rein. Right foot out of the stirrup. Over, feet together, drop. That's good. Now run your stirrups up the outside leather to the top, like this. Good, lift the saddle flap up, so, and loosen

the girths three holes. Now the men can get on
with their work. Keep coming regularly and we shall
all be riding in the next National."

Mr. Wisp entered his office, and they watched
the men washing the horses' feet, hissing, hissing,
all the time. Old Bob looked at John with a keen
smile in his black beady eyes.

" Well, sir, did ye enjoy yourself ? "

" Yes, thank you. Grand fun."

" Ah, he's a good instructor is the Guv'nor—
you couldn't have a better. Says what he means,
and means what he says. A good man to go, too."

" What do you mean by that ? "

" A good man to hounds. A good horseman, with
pluck, nerve, and an eye for picking a country. Goes
easily without knocking his horse up, and yet takes
his fences as they come. Irish Jack here used to be
second horseman to the Duke of Buckstone, and
he'll tell ye something about hunting ; won't ye,
Jack ? "

" I will that ; all mud and glory, and the divil
for company. Did you ever see a hunt now,
missy ? "

" No, but we may do so one day, although I
think it's rather cruel."

" Then you've missed the grandest sight the
world has to offer. I've seen the Duke's hounds
going like a flock of pigeons, with the little red
varmint two fields ahead, running so fast they hadn't
breath to speak, and the gintlemen toiling after
them without breath to swear, and the leaps coming

so big and fast it's a wonder the horses weren't killed ; and the mud flying so thick the scarlet looked like blood, and the grey sky with its wracks of clouds like the day of doom—ah, his day of doom it was and an eight-mile point at that, with hardly a check."

Jane looked askance at John.

" Sounds queer to me," he said.

" Mr. Wisp 'll explain all that to you one day, Captain," said Bob. "Come along, Mary, old girl."

" How big is Mary ? "

" Do you mean how ' big ' is she, or how ' tall ' ? The height of a horse is not his size ; there are big little 'uns and little big 'uns. Mary is a good-sized pony, and she'd be fourteen hands three inches in height. You measure the height from the highest point of the withers—here, just in front of the saddle. Four inches measure the hand, so fourteen hands three inches would be fifty-nine inches, or four feet eleven inches high. We had a gentleman here once who asked whose hands we used to measure with, because he said some would be smaller than others."

The feet were finished. Old Bob took Mary, Irish Jack Polly, and a young lad the grey to the stables as Mr. Wisp reappeared from the office.

" Have you any sugar left for Peppermint, the young strawberry roan I promised to show you ? Come on then."

In a loose box he stood ; a five-year-old of outstanding quality; crushed strawberry and cream in colour with dark points. A beautiful clear bold eye, set in a small head of delicate proportions; powerful quarters and good thighs.

"Come in," said Mr. Wisp, opening the box door, "he's as gentle as a dove. Well, Peppermint, old man, and how are you?" The horse rubbed against him, gently rumbling in his nostrils. "We shall have some fun one day. See how freely he moves? To see him now you wouldn't think he could play up, would you? But he'll grow out of it with time and patience."

As the horse finished munching the piece of sugar Jane gave him, he lifted his head and ran his tongue over her cheek. She felt thrilled, and rather excited, and just a little nervous.

"Don't be afraid," said Mr. Wisp. "Watch him take a piece from my mouth," and putting a piece of sugar between his lips he put his face close to Peppermint. Delicately the horse took the tit-bit.

"There—good boy—enough for now."

"I love him," said Jane. "Don't you, John?"

"He looks a topper. Hope I shall be able to ride him one day. But I suppose it'll be years before I've enough experience, won't it, Mr. Wisp?"

"Well, he needs a good horseman on him at the moment." His shrewd grey eyes looked kindly at John, and he added, as he saw the quick flash of disappointment pass like a cloud over the lad's keen young face, "We'll see what we can do in a few weeks' time, when Carew has ridden him. If he comes all right, and you get on, he'd carry you better than most, as there's nothing so kind and generous as a thoroughbred."

" Thanks awfully. I say, Jane, we've forgotten to give the sixpences Dad gave us for the men. Can we go this way ? "

As they walked to the other end of the stable, both picking their feet up, Jane asked why grooms hiss so much as they work.

" It's a habit, and they don't know when they do it, but really it's to prevent the very fine dust which comes out of a horse's coat from going down the throat as they groom. The effects from it can be serious, although cases of illness are very rare : I think I've only heard of one in my life. Once grooms start the hissing habit, they do it all the time. Old Bob even does it when he reads a newspaper ! "

The men were actively cleaning the horses, or " strapping," as they call it, coats off and braces down.

" Thank you, milady," said Bob, as he spat for luck on the sixpence Jane gave him before pocketing it.

" Thank you, sir," said Irish Jack, " 'tis the silver lining to the day."

As they came out of the stable a sports car drove into the yard, and from it emerged a tall, clean-shaven young man about thirty. He was quietly dressed in a lounge sports suit, the side slits at the coat back betraying the horseman. His face was clean cut, with a fresh complexion, a rather thin mouth, and open, very level blue eyes. He looked,

33

what in fact he was, a typical Englishman, active and lithe in body, the breadth of shoulders indicating strength.

" Hallo, Wisp ! " said he, " I've just run over to see the lion."

" Ah ! " said Mr. Wisp, his face expressing his pleasure, " we've just been to look at him. Not much lion about him, more like a lamb."

" I see, a wolf in sheep's clothing. One of those nice, quiet innocent-looking horses that are so good for taking the conceit out of one. New pupils ? "

" Yes, just had their first ride. This is Miss Jane Vanster and her brother John. Of course, Jane, you can guess who this is. Mr. James Carew, who is going to exercise his powerful personality on Peppermint. Mr. Carew rides as an amateur jockey in steeplechases, but doesn't like it mentioned in public."

Jane eyed him gravely, thinking he wasn't a bit like Steve Donoghue or any of the other jockeys she had seen on the films, whilst John, a little bolder, asked, " Why don't you like it mentioned in public ? "

" Well, I think one has a right to keep one's errors private. Also as a rule, immediately people know I race they expect me to give them tips and make their fortunes, but as a matter of fact the men who ride races usually know less than anybody. They know when they've got a chance to win, but I think it is better to remain silent and be thought a fool than speak and remove all doubt. Eh, Wisp ? "

34

" Quite."

" Did you enjoy your ride ? "

" Rather, should think we did."

" Well, I hope you don't remember all this old fox has told you ? You did ? You do ? Fine. Wisp, they don't know you yet. But joking apart, remember half he tells you, and you'll soon ride like centaurs."

" Did Mr. Wisp teach you ? "

"I did, Jane," broke in the riding master. "Come into my office and I'll show you an interesting photograph."

" I say, Wisp, spare my blushes."

" You go and look at the horse. He's in number three box."

The office was the most fascinating place they had ever seen. Very neat and tidy; green baize-lined glass cases on the walls containing various bits, polished like silver ; several bridles not in everyday use, the leather as soft as silk ; a large bookshelf with books of intriguing titles—*The Horse as Comrade and Friend*, *Points of the Horse*, *Thoughts on Hunting* being three that caught John's eye. An office desk methodically pigeon-holed; a telephone; a table containing tea service laid with two cups ; two armchairs by the fireplace, on which a polished kettle was near the boil; and numerous photographs of horses, harness horses, polo ponies, hunters, meets of hounds, coaches, surrounded a delightful picture by Lionel Edwardes.

" Why," said Jane, " it looks as if you live here ! "

" I do. That door leads to my bedroom, and beyond that is the bathroom, which I had built recently."

" Aren't you lonely sometimes ? "

" I might be if I weren't fond of reading. It's very snug here of a winter's evening, with the fire on, a good book and the old pipe, and the occasional stamp of horses. Besides, I start very early in the morning, you know. Would you like it here, John ? "

" Yes, I should. It's a *man's* place. Which is the photograph ? "

" There it is. ' J. Carew on Saucy Sue, 1920.' He was fourteen then, and won a lot of prizes with that pony. A little devil she was with anybody she didn't know, but he and she made a perfect combination."

" What happened to her ? "

" I sold her very well. She died of heart failure out hunting four years afterwards."

" What bad luck. Do many horses die of that ? "

" Well, more than most people would think."

The kettle started to sing as Carew joined them, and the stable clock struck once.

" Heavens," said Jane, " that's half-past five. Come on, John. We're supposed to be home by now."

" Right-o—I could spend a week here. What's that brass band with the leather each end, Mr. Wisp ? "

" A mud scraper. You hold it in two hands,

36

bend it, and draw it over a horse's body. It scrapes off all the water and mud or sweat in hot weather. They use them on polo ponies after a chukka, when sluicing down. But don't ask any more questions. John, your sister's getting impatient." He smiled at Jane who held out her hand to him.

"Good-bye, Mr. Wisp. *Come on*, John! We'll be here the same time next week. Good-bye, Mr. Carew."

"Good-bye. By the way, put a little common soda in your bath to-night. It'll remove any stiffness. I find it invaluable, especially as I'm always falling about the country. We shall see more of each other, you know."

. . . . .

"Grand chap, old Wisp," said John as they hurried home.

"I liked Mr. Carew too," replied Jane.

CHAPTER FIVE

" KEEP THEM IN YOUR POCKET "

CHRISTMAS was followed by a spell of mild
weather such as is only to be found in our
winter climate, and although it was very disappoint-
ing to the skating and tobogganing enthusiast, it was
greatly appreciated by Jane and John, who were thus
enabled to ride a good deal during the holidays.

In the four months since their first lesson they
had made rapid strides, fulfilling the promise then
shown. Each Saturday had been eagerly awaited,
and such had been their keenness that Mr. Wisp
had taken a vital interest in their advancement.
He was too good an instructor to be dilatory with
any pupil, but human nature must prevail, and in
their case teaching had developed into a friend-
ship.

Riding, once the first initial stages are over, is
the most fascinating of pastimes, and it is no wonder
that horses, and everything connected with them,
become a passion with some people. So it was with
Jane and John. They had learnt to love the creak
of the saddle beneath them and the view between
keen ears pricked well forward; the smell of the

38

stables and the occasional stamp or snort of horses feeding. Of course they still had a great deal to learn, and affected by the example of Mr. Wisp's own modesty would modestly admit how little they knew.

They were more than popular with the men; Irish Jack would do anything for Jane, whilst John was a favourite with a red and round-faced, blue-eyed north-countryman, who had now been with Mr. Wisp about two months. Known as " Darby " all his life throughout the length and breadth of England, it is to be doubted whether his own mother knew him as anything else.

He had seen service with countless masters—stud groom here; strapping in hunt stables there; with show jumpers to Germany; with polo ponies to America. Excellent at his job, he was not to be relied on by any employer for keeps owing to his desire for incessant change.

This desire was sometimes caused by a little failing of running into small debts. He would say, with a broad grin splitting his face from ear to ear, " I'd best be on, sir." Next day he was gone, and the day after round would come his creditors, but no one ever knew his next destination. Despite this he was a likeable fellow, a good worker, and still of a very active disposition despite his sixty odd years. He was scrupulously clean, always washing himself to such an extent indeed that his countenance literally shone.

As Jane and John entered the yard this particular

morning he was vigorously drying his face on a clean towel watched by a small boy, dressed like themselves in jodhpurs, but wearing a quartered school cap.

"Hallo, Peter," John said, "waiting for your bath ? 'Morning, Darby."

"Good-morning, sir. Good-morning, miss. Master Peter's just asked me why I wash so much ; says he doesn't care about it. Clean man, clean horse, says I."

"You storyteller," said Peter, "I didn't. And I'm not waiting for a bath either. Tease me and I'll fight you. I'm going to find Mr. Wisp. Come with me, Jane ? "

"Yes, I'll come. Aren't some more people coming this morning, Peter ? "

"Oh yes. We're going to have a talk an' do all sorts of things. Do *you* know where a horse's cannon bone is ? Darby told me it was next to his pistol joint. *I* don't believe he's got a pistol joint."

"Neither do I. There's Mr. Wisp, we'll ask him."

Mr. Wisp, quiet and dignified as usual, came from the stables accompanied by Miss Cushion, a somewhat stout lady of uncertain age, who had lately taken up riding, showing an almost pathetic desire to learn, and a smart, attractive young woman named Miss Stuart. Miss Stuart kept a horse of her own at livery with Mr. Wisp, and, whilst being admired by Jane, was rather envied by John. She was another tribute to Mr. Wisp's teaching, and although she had graduated from the " passive " to the " active " stage of riding, never missed a chance to improve her knowledge.

She had come to-day because it was arranged that several people should spend the whole day, during which Mr. Wisp intended to explain many things in the course of a talk, with practical tuition in the paddock and stables to follow.

This was his idea, and although he knew that it would be impossible to get together a number of people of equal proficiency, he thought that if the beginners absorbed only half the information it would help them. For instance young Peter could hardly be expected to understand everything, and, fond as he was of the boy, amused by his many antics and old-fashioned ways, he would rather have left him out. But hear what he says :

" Good-morning, Miss Jane. You know Miss Cushion and Miss Stuart, don't you ? Going to be fine when we ride later. Hallo, Peter."

" Please, Mr. Wisp, has a horse got a pistol joint ? "

Mr. Wisp looked puzzled until Jane explained the situation.

" Ah, I see," he exclaimed, smiling. " No, Peter, it hasn't. You go and tell Darby not to pull your leg."

Peter ran off.

" That boy's as sharp as a needle. I didn't really want him to come to-day, but I felt he would have been so disappointed. He goes to a school where there are four hundred boys, and I believe he's the smallest in it. They call him Carnera! His father tells me that if ever there's a scrap, young Peter's at the bottom of it. Always ready to fight. But he'll be a good lad in time if he's handled right. Here comes Miss Allen, so we're only waiting for Robin Briscoe and we can start. . . . How are you to-day, Miss Allen? Glad to see you managed to get the day off from the office."

"Very well, thanks. Yes, luckily there was a holiday due to me. Quite a bright party to-day I see. Are you staying with us, Miss Stuart, or are you off for a ride by yourself ? "

"No, I'm staying. Mr. Wisp has been up all night swotting information with which to astonish the ignorant. Now confess, Mr. Wisp."

His grey eyes twinkled as he blandly remarked :

"Hardly that, but I have done a little preparation ; as you'll see later, eh, Miss Allen ? "

"That's our secret," she laughed, " But we must be careful or Jane will be suspicious."

"Have you seen Mr. Carew lately ? " asked Jane.

"No, not for a week or two. He's been very busy racing and hunting."

"He has a nice life," said Miss Allen. "Does he not have to work ? "

"No," said Mr. Wisp, " he has a small private income which he supplements by buying and selling one or two young horses a year. He bought Peppermint from me a few weeks ago."

"Did he really!" exclaimed Miss Stuart. "Has he taken him away?"

"Not yet. He's boxed him down for several days' hunting. He says Peppermint has the heart of a lion. Never turns his head from a fence."

"How marvellous! Does he still rear?"

"Well, he's nearly got over that. Carew has spent hours on him. He's a very patient fellow, quiet but strong, and knows that it's absolutely fatal to hit a thoroughbred. He's ridden out of these gates and back again some days, I should say, if once, a hundred times in a morning. First of all Peppermint stood on his hind legs, as if he'd never come down again. All Carew used was his voice quietly and his spurs."

"Spurs!" broke in Miss Cushion. "How cruel."

"Well, Miss Cushion, a man must be master of his horse, or the horse would become incorrigible. There are all sorts of theories about curing horses that rear. Some say break a bottle of water, or red-coloured water, over his head. Others advocate a rope from his foreleg to the rider, which the rider pulls and brings the horse to his knees before he can rear. Another method is to lean forward and strike the hind legs with a long whip whilst the horse is poised.

"I don't believe in any of these. Mind you, they may have been tried successfully here and there, but fundamentally when a horse rears, what you've got to do is to remove his stance from his hind quarters. With time and patience spurs and the voice will do

43

it. A horse's reasoning powers are limited, but he eventually realizes that immediately he stands up his ribs become uncomfortable, and the rider still remains immovable.

" As a young man I once spent three hours on a young horse in a pen of sheep hurdles. He jumped in well, and then wouldn't jump out. Refused and reared. The fight between us had been coming for a long time, and I welcomed it. During all that time I never hit him once, but every time he reared pressed the spurs against him. At last he gave in and jumped out. I don't know which was the hotter, he or I. But I do know that afterwards he never gave any trouble and became a bold, brilliant hunter."

." Well," said Miss Cushion, still not satisfied that men who use such methods ought not to be locked up, " are the spurs sharp ? "

" No," replied Mr. Wisp, hoping to remove any misunderstanding, " they are not. Sharp spurs are no good because they only prick and the pierced part soon becomes numb. A blunt spur is the one to use, so that the horse comes to fear the pressure on his skin and muscles."

" Oh, I see," said Miss Cushion once more. " Then he wouldn't bleed ? "

" Not at all," said Mr. Wisp, smiling inwardly at the lady's simple and not uncommon idea that an animal is not hurt if it doesn't bleed. To close the matter he said, " I don't advocate the use of spurs at all, Miss Cushion. On inexperienced heels they

44

cause unnecessary pain and suffering, and usually the more inexperienced people are the greater their desire to wear them. I have many times said, ' Wear them *off* your horse as much as you like, but please, when mounted, keep them in your pocket ! '

" Last year a foreigner came to ride one of my horses. He was highly recommended by a lady client ; but, of course, as soon as he came into the yard it was obvious how much he knew, because his spurs were on upside down. I was out at the time, and Old Bob tried as tactfully as he could to get him to remove them. He was most indignant. ' I 'ave rode ze 'orse,' said he, ' up ze 'ills of Spain and down ze valleys of Shermany, and to remove my spurs I 'ave nevair been asked ! '

" ' Have it your own way,' said Bob, and out he went.

" Well, the horse became so irritated by the spurs that he went faster and faster, until our widely travelled horseman thought the horse was bolting and lost his head. Then, of course, the horse did bolt, through fear. One thing that really upsets a horse is for him to lose confidence in his rider. That's why I always say to you people, ' Keep calm, don't lose your head, there is plenty of time.' "

" What happened to your foreigner ? " asked Jane.

" Eventually he got exhausted and fell off. The horse came home here, and so did he by a car in which some one kindly gave him a lift.

" Entering the yard in a rage he said, ' 'Ow dare

you send me out on such a terrible 'orse ? 'E is not safe. I will take the action at law ! '

" ' Well, sir,' said Old Bob, knowing that all hope of a tip was gone, ' you've got your spurs on upside down. Now, if I was you, and I wanted people in this country to know I was a good horseman—a *good* horseman, mark you—I'd wear them things on my elbows.'

"Our foreigner, looking at Bob's grinning face, and also that of Irish Jack and a gentleman just come in, decided the English were a bad lot, and left."

" I never knew such a man as you for amusing anecdotes," said Miss Stuart, " and they always get the point home."

"A *bon mot*," said Miss Cushion; "very good, Miss Stuart."

"What's a *bon mot* ? " asked Peter, who had gently inserted himself in front of Jane and Miss Stuart, and for the last five minutes had been standing looking up at Mr. Wisp. Before any one explained he shouted, " Hurrah ! Here's Robin. You're late, and have kept us all waiting."

Robin Briscoe was a youth of seventeen who had begun riding a month or so before the Vansters. He was somewhat slower in thought than they were, and showed less aptitude. But although slow, he was also sure, and once anything entered his brain, it was there for good. He apologized for being late.

" Never mind," said Miss Allen, " I haven't been here so long myself."

" Mr. Wisp's been telling us about a man that wears his spurs on his elbows," said Peter.

" Now, then, Peter," smiled Mr. Wisp. " Well, every one's here and it's a quarter to ten, so if you'll come into my office we'll make a start with the day's work. Peter, please run and find John."

CHAPTER SIX

THE GOOD HORSEMAN

EXTRA chairs had been put in the office, and they all managed to get comfortably settled. A cheerful fire blazed on the hearth, glinting on the brass and steel.

" Now," said Mr. Wisp, " you've all come here for the day, which I have carefully scheduled into a programme that I hope will be as interesting as it will be instructive. I am quite aware that in some schools of thought the curriculum would not be approved, partly because it would be said I try to cram too much information in at one sitting, as it were. That's as may be. The difficulty lies in getting a number of people together at the same time and on numerous occasions. This is not a school, and you come here for pleasure. It's my job to teach you as much as I can about riding and about horses, and although I have no doubt that you will forget a lot that I say, the point is that it will come back to you from time to time when I have occasion to mention it again.

" Some of you are further advanced than others. If you already know what I'm saying, I can rely upon you to be patient for the sake of those who don't.

" The first thing I'm going to talk about is a good horseman ; what he is, and the things that make him what he is.

" There is no doubt at all that some people have a more natural flair for riding than others. This does not mean that some people will never ride well. If properly taught, and possessing the grit to persevere, there is no one who could not ride passably well. The only exceptions are the extremely nervous and the very rough.

" Shape and build are a help or a hindrance as the case may be ; very few people are the ideal shape for riding, yet some of the world's finest horsemen are men of whom it would not be said, at the first glance, ' He's the ideal make.'

" But to ' cut the cackle and come to the 'osses,' as Mr. Jorrocks would say.

" I should define a good horseman as a man, or woman, who through temperament, knowledge, and experience rides well, and also looks well on a horse.

" I use the term ' horseman,' and shall continue to do so, ladies, as it is easier, but you will understand that I mean ' horsewoman ' as well.

" He looks part of his horse. He sits lightly and flexibly, but very firmly, in his saddle. His body harmonizes with every pace, whether walking, trotting, cantering, galloping, or jumping. Not only does his body harmonize, but his hands also. Indeed one could not do without the other.

" Now how has he arrived at this perfect state

49

of synchronization with his horse? It has no doubt taken him a long time. Perhaps, you will think, his opportunities have been many. In my own experience it is not the rich man, who can afford countless horses and lessons, who necessarily turns into a good horseman. It is more often the man of moderate means with the desire to get the most for his money, and to profit as quickly as possible from his lessons.

" By ' profit quickly ' I do not mean rushing. I mean the man who is willing to practise what he's told and who is not conceited about his progress. If you wish to ride well, abhor swank, abhor conceit. The good horseman has neither. He has cultivated gentleness, quickness, sympathy with his horse, and determination.

" I mention determination because the rider must control the horse. A horse likes to obey, and provided he has enough confidence in his rider, will go anywhere and do anything—through fire, through water, over obstacles. When too much is asked of him, and he gets hurt, then he loses confidence. But his is a generous nature, and the good horseman is one who does not take too much advantage of it.

" I said sympathy. By this I mean understanding and appreciation. Sometimes one sees a horse fidgeting, and the rider complains because he is not having a comfortable ride. The good horseman would not complain. He would say the *horse* was not having a comfortable journey, and would try to find the reason why. It might be that the saddle was pinching or the bit too sharp. The horse might have a sore mouth or back. Failing these, or similar external signs, the good horseman would ask himself what *he* was doing wrong.

" In the hunting field horses sometimes refuse at a fence. Many a time have I seen a horse punished for it, and yet how likely is it that he was not presented at it properly, or that his stride was not quite right for him to make a big enough effort to clear it at one bound ? In circumstances such as these the good horseman will turn round, take the horse back far enough, and not too far, to try again ; pat him and speak to him. How generously then will his mount respond and leap as if he were never coming back to earth. Alternatively he will try the fence at another place, with the same successful leap. *That* is understanding and appreciation.

" To possess sympathy with your horse does not necessarily mean that you must understand how to cure lameness or how to treat him for strangles, but does mean that you should know when his tackle is comfortable, and how to take it off or put it on. That you know when he is really playing up or shying through fear at some alarming monstrosity of a bus or lorry. That you do not mistake his playful leap on first coming out of his stable and getting on grass to a deliberate attempt to throw you off, or ask him to canter on a slippery tarmac road or gallop through deep stiff holding mud.

" Perhaps the best way to define sympathy

would be to say that a good horseman '*thinks with his horse.*'

"What is it, Peter? You look as if you want to ask something."

"Mr. Wisp, would Tinker go through fire?"

"Certainly, if he had enough confidence in *you*. We'll try one day.

"Well, I've explained two qualities of the good

horseman. Sympathy and determination. The other two are simple. Quickness is the rapid and neat manipulation of the reins and the aids. The aids are the rider's legs, his hands, and his voice. I have taught you all the manipulation of the reins and the use of the legs. Quickness only comes with constant practice.

"Good hands is a subject about which volumes have been written, and I do not intend to confuse you with a complicated treatise on them. Suffice it to say that no man is a good horseman without good hands, and he cannot have these without a strong, firm seat, which makes his balance entirely independent of his horse's mouth. His hands thus become the most sensitive connection in controlling his horse. The voice brings me to gentleness. By gentleness I do not mean softness. As I said before, horses like to obey, and expect to obey. But at the same time they are human enough to like their own way sometimes, and it is at such times as these that the rider must be firm but not rough. Roughness will provoke trouble. The horse is a sensitive creature, and although he may be doing wrong in your eyes, it may be unconsciously on his part. If corrected roughly, therefore, he will become alarmed, and do something else perhaps even more disconcerting to the rider.

" A quiet gentle voice and quiet gentle handling will not alarm him. Some people mistake gentleness for *letting* the horse have his own way. For example, a young woman I taught a year or two ago progressed extremely well up to a point. She had a good seat, fair hands, and perseverance. One day she was riding a young horse of mine, whose education was nearly complete. I rode with her. This young horse was high-couraged, and as so often happens, instead of walking, he was apt to prance along at a pace between a walk and a trot. It's a most uncomfortable pace, and if not checked becomes a habit. It is the duty of the rider therefore to *make* his horse walk. I told her several times to do so, until she finally said, ' Oh, let him do it, bless him. He *likes* doing it.'

" That's not gentleness, that's softness. Nothing I could say would make her alter her view. She thought the horse ought to be allowed to go as he liked, and as long as she holds that view she will never become a good horsewoman.

" Yes, Miss Cushion, do you want to ask something ? "

" Why is the prancing pace you describe wrong ? "

" Because at that pace the horse is not collected ; he's unbalanced, and through being so is uncomfortable to ride. Think how tiring it would be to ride him all day.

" We now see that a good horseman possesses gentleness, sympathy, quickness, and determination, which, combined, make the correct temperament. Constant practice has given him a firm seat and good hands. Application has given him knowledge and experience. Reasoning has taught him something about tackle. He has no conceit, and is *always* willing to learn. When one sees him riding, either quietly hacking or following hounds across country, he seems to be going without effort. It is an ideal picture to which we should all aspire. In the early stages of learning how far off does such perfection seem ! Yet we should not despair, but remember *he* once began, and is only an example of lessons well learnt. Before I go on, has any one any questions ? "

54

"Yes, I have, please," said John. "When a horse—I mean a famous racehorse—refuses in a steeplechase, what is the cause, because he wouldn't have an inexperienced horseman riding him?"

"Well," said Mr. Wisp, "in a race there is not enough time to try again. Too much ground has been lost. All sorts of things may happen. The horse probably didn't get his stride in right, or he may have done too much jumping. They do

get sick of it, you know. Very likely the same horse, with a different jockey up, would win races later in faultless style. Racehorses get very knowing, and sometimes a change of jockey does them good, without there being the slightest reflection on the one displaced."

"How long does it take to become a tolerably good rider, Mr. Wisp?" said Miss Allen.

"I've been expecting that question," he replied. "It depends entirely upon the opportunity and ability of the pupil.   A person who can ride four times a week has a great advantage over one who can only do so once or twice.   But given a favourable ability, they are level in the number of lessons or rides required.   I should say it takes from fifty to seventy lessons—some people less, some more.

" In that time one should develop confidence, grip, and balance, and be ready to proceed with quite advanced work.   All need not be individual instructional lessons, of course, provided the pupil continues to practise his teaching, and is not content to merely slop along.   One sees many people trotting and cantering by themselves, who don't know, do not trouble, or have forgotten even how to sit correctly."

" Thank you," said Miss Allen.   " Then there's hope for us all."

CHAPTER SEVEN

THE HORSE

" NOW," said Mr. Wisp, "having considered the main qualities of the good horseman, we will spend a few minutes talking of the horse which carries him.

" In addition to the rider's qualities I have just mentioned are good nerves and good temper. Good nerves are really part of determination. Most people have fairly steady nerves, and it is only in exceptional cases that one finds, or there is any need for, iron nerves.

" Good temper is a different matter, and as the horse is a very sensitive animal he is quickly affected by the temper of the man on him. Any one, therefore, who is naturally quick-tempered, hasty, or easily irritated, and yet desirous of becoming even a moderately good horseman, must curb his natural impulses with the exercise of patience.

" When I say the horse is a sensitive animal I don't mean that he is super-sensitive. But we must remember that he is subject to man from his earliest days, and that, as I have said before, his reasoning powers are limited.

" This is easy enough to prove, because he relies upon his past experience for his reasoning power. Thus if I were to place a jump at a certain spot in a field, and by that jump to place a pole, a wheel-barrow, or any object to serve as a landmark, and jump a horse over the obstacle for several days in succession, and then remove the fence, but leave the landmark still there, the horse would still jump at that spot as if the fence were there. Although he could not see the fence, he would still think it existed. You may have seen horses jump ' invisible fences,' as they are called, in a circus. Next time see if you can spot the landmark.

" The horse is very highly couraged, but for centuries his chief defence has been his vigility and ability to escape from danger at a great speed. In other words, his instinct is to be suspicious of any strange thing or person. Ride a horse on an accustomed track, and then see him shy away from a branch which has been blown down in the night. *You* know what it is immediately, for you can reason. *He* doesn't, but thinks, ' What's that ? It wasn't there yesterday—will it hurt me ? I'll see it doesn't. I'll get out of striking distance at once,' and therefore leaps to one side.

" The better bred a horse is the more highly strung and sensitive he is. There is no point in my discussing anything but riding horses to-day.

" The thoroughbred or ' blood horse ' is the ideal horse. In him is combined resolute courage, speed, stamina, intelligence, and by his fine construction

58

his movements are easy and flowing, so that at all paces he is the most comfortable ride.

"The most famous stallion was a horse named the Godolphin Barb, and from him are descended many of our present day racehorses. He was a Barb from Northern Africa, and was imported to this country from France, where his quality was not understood, as according to tradition he was degraded. there to drawing a wood cart in Paris. He stood at the stud of Lord Godolphin in Cambridgeshire, where he sired many colts and fillies in the early eighteenth century. He had a beautifully set-on head with an uncommonly fine muzzle, a very prominent crest, deep and oblique shoulders, wide loins, and well let down and powerful quarters. He was great friends with a cat for many years, and at his death in 1753, when he was twenty-nine years old, the cat pined away with grief.

"There are comparatively few thoroughbreds out of the great number bred that have outstanding success on the turf, and it is those that don't which come into other hands for breeding, hunting, and hacking, so that we also get the horses which are not quite thoroughbred but nearly so. A thoroughbred stallion is mated with a strong commoner mare, and we get a big powerful hunter, with the speed and quality of his father, and the size and jumping quarters of his mother. But I'm not going into all the intricate details of breeding, and shall stick to the blood horse as our ideal.

"His most characteristic features are the smallness

The drawing showed a horse in outline, the various points being named, surrounded by a lettered border. "No foot, no horse; no hock, no hunter; the longer the rein the better the ride; four inches equals one hand; keep *your* hands low."

"Why do so many horses come from Ireland ? " asked Robin Briscoe suddenly, after he had carefully studied his drawing.

"Because the soil is particularly suitable to breed them, apart from Irishmen being so fond of horses," replied Mr. Wisp. "The soil contains a great proportion of lime, which is a bone-building nutriment. It is not generally known, or I suppose not really considered by any one not actively connected with breeding, that the soil on which a horse spends the early days of his life affects his growth and substance to a great extent.

"The length of legs with which a horse is foaled determines his ultimate height to some degree but does not determine his actual size. Height and size are different things. It is possible to have a powerful horse on short legs, well developed in muscle and bone—what we call a ' big little one.' Alternatively to have a tall horse, leggy and slack, which is called a ' little big one.' One may have been bred on good soil and one on bad. I believe Old Bob mentioned that to you on the first day, John?"

"Yes, he did. I wondered what on earth he meant. What *I* want to know is, how do you tell a horse's age ? "

" I know," broke in Peter.   " Never look a gift horse in the mouth."

" Well," said Mr. Wisp, " why ? "

" Because," he replied, " the teeth might tell you he's older than you think."

" Right, my lad," said Mr. Wisp.   " I'll show you." He fetched a book from the case, and opening it said, " There's a diagram here which will help me to explain it.   A horse has twelve front teeth,

7 YEARS OLD

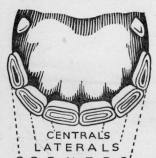

CENTRALS
LATERALS
C O R N E R S

12 YEARS OLD

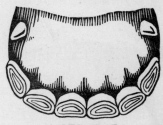

NOTE THE
DIFFERENCE
IN SHAPE

called incisors, six in the upper jaw and six in the lower.   When he is five years old he has what is known as ' a full mouth.'   That means a complete set of permanent incisor teeth.   Up to then, from two and a half years, he has been changing the first set, known as ' milk teeth.'   Well, at five years old he has the teeth which will last him through life, and in the top of each tooth is a black or dark spot, known as a ' mark.'   Starting from the centre each way, these marks disappear each year.   So the two centres have gone by the time he is six, the next by seven, and the last by eight. The two centre teeth are called centrals, the two next laterals, and the two outside corners. The tops of the teeth, in which are the marks, are called ' tables.' The lower jaw is the one to examine."

" What causes the marks to disappear ? " asked Miss Allen.

" The friction of the top teeth on the lower," replied Mr. Wisp. " After nine years to tell the age becomes rather an expert's job, and I'm afraid a little in advance of our talk to-day."

" Do tell us," said Jane. " We'd rather like to know."

" All right, I will. But don't blame me if you forget it."

" We won't," said Miss Stuart ; " but it's as well to have the whole story, isn't it, John ? "

" Rather."

" Well, then," said Mr. Wisp, " the marks have completely disappeared at nine. After this changes come in the shape of the teeth. The tables, instead of being elongated and oval, become triangular in shape, beginning yearly again. When the horse is nine years old the tables of the centrals assume a triangular shape, at ten the tables of the laterals do the same, and at eleven the corners also. Of course, this change does not take place suddenly but very gradually, as it is caused by the wearing away of the teeth. After eleven the triangular shape becomes even more pronounced, but it is then almost impossible to tell the exact age. As he gets older the teeth become more and more in a sloping position in the gums, so that without any other guide it is comparatively easy to tell an old horse.

" Other indications of an old horse are hollows above the eyes, which become greater as time goes on, and grey hairs about the eyes. In the case of grey horses, their coat becomes of a lighter colour each year, and they eventually turn white, or nearly so. The front legs also show signs of wear, sometimes being bent at the knee; but indications of age, wear, and tear are entirely dependent upon the work a horse has done and the care which has been taken of him."

" Thank you," said Miss Stuart. " But what of the time before five ? "

" I'm afraid that is *too* complicated," said Mr. Wisp. " All I shall tell you is that the first teeth— the milk teeth—are small and white. These also change for the permanent in the order of centrals, laterals, and corners, commencing at two and a half years old.

" At some time or other you will probably hear the term ' rising six ' or ' six off.' Supposing a horse is nearly six, say within a few months of that age, he is said to be rising six, and if a month or two over that age he is said to be six off. The same applies to any other age of course, and as foals are usually born in the spring each year of a horse's age is completed in the spring."

" I shall never learn all that," said Miss Cushion in a tone of despair.

" Cheer up," said Miss Allen ; " we can't all be bright, you know."

" Yes, but I'm so dense."

" Never mind," said Mr. Wisp. " In a few months' time things won't seem so strange. Later on we'll have a quiet talk about it by ourselves."

CHAPTER EIGHT

ROBIN WOULD LIKE TO BE A VET

"WHAT is the average age to which a horse lives?" asked Jane.

"Until he has an accident and is destroyed, as a rule. Racehorses begin racing at two years old, and most of them retire to stud, or from racing, by five—flat racing that is. Those that go in for steeplechasing don't usually start until five, and go on until twelve or more. Hunters are broken in at four, ridden gently to hounds at five, and in their prime at seven and eight.

"Barring accidents, a hunter can work until he's twenty. The best horse I ever rode over timber fences was twenty when I bought him. He was only a little horse, but very strong, and would rather jump a gate when hounds were running than wait for me to open it.

"Many a horse has even lived to thirty. Ben, the bay you'll ride to-day, Miss Cushion, is about seventeen. He makes a noise, but is otherwise sound."

"Whatever does that mean?" she asked.

"It means," he replied, "an unsoundness of wind, of which there are three kinds—roaring, whistling, and broken wind. They are all incurable, and although horses so affected can still work, it detracts greatly from their market value. But there is no need for you to be alarmed, Miss Cushion. Ben is quite capable of doing the work you will require of him to-day.

" He is a whistler. This is usually due to paralysis of the left vocal chord, so that if put to severe exertion he emits a shrill whistling sound. It is the mildest form of unsoundness of wind. I'm afraid I spoke rather loosely when I said he makes a noise. He does technically, but usually the term is applied to roaring, which is more severe and more apparent. Roaring is an acute and developed paralysis of the same vocal chord, whilst broken wind has its seat in the lungs, due to rupture of some of the air cells."

" What causes unsoundness of wind ? " said Miss Allen. " Sorry, you people, but I'm a glutton for information."

" Don't mind us," said Miss Stuart; "we're all here to learn. Go on, Mr. Wisp."

" It's supposed to be hereditary. But it's a certain fact that short-necked, thick-necked horses are subject to it, and also those which are narrow chested. After all, the function of a horse's breathing is the same as in man—to take in air, which, passing through the lungs, gives oxygen to the heart, thus purifying the blood, and generating heat and energy.

" A horse's work, being so much greater in energy

68

than man's, necessitates a powerful breathing system, and if he is constructionally small, so that his lungs and heart are cramped, the air cells are liable to rupture under pressure. If such a horse is over-exerted or overworked when young, the strain affects his wind. A horse suffering from unsoundness of wind, when galloped too fast or too far, will eventually labour and stop. The air supply is not sufficient for the work the heart is called upon to do. All the same, he is quite capable of doing gentle work. Over-exertion will produce broken wind, and a severe cold or strangles are sometimes responsible for whistling or roaring."

" Is there no cure at all ? " asked Jane.

" No certain cure. There is an operation in which the larynx is opened up and the vocal chord made to adhere to the side of the larynx. I believe this has been successful in some cases, although there is no guarantee of permanency. There is also another, known as ' tubing.'

" In this case a hole is made direct to the windpipe and a metal tube inserted. It is sometimes performed on a horse just before a race, and they have been known to win. I remember one famous horse named War Gratuity, who was tubed and won a great many point - to - point races. I think nineteen in all. The tube has to be kept very clean, and well vaselined before re-insertion, or it is painful. I have been told that if the tube is kept in for two years the flesh will heal and deaden, leaving a permanent hole. If the operation is performed for one race or so only, and the tube not put back, the wound will heal in the normal way."

" Horses seem to have funny things go wrong with them," said Robin, who had been listening intently. " I should like to be a vet."

" If one stopped to remember all one knows of the possibilities in that direction," said Mr. Wisp, shaking his head, " one would never buy any horses at all."

" Do tell us some more," said Miss Stuart.

" I'm afraid there isn't time to-day. It will be a very full day as it is."

Peter and John had been putting their heads together over the diagrams. Peter looked puzzled, and John's explanation being unsatisfactory, he said :

" Please, Mr. Wisp, what does, ' No foot, no horse,' and ' No hock, no hunter,' mean ? "

" Now we get back to the original theme," said Mr. Wisp. " ' No foot, no horse,' is a very old saying, but still true. A horse's feet have to carry him over country, plough or grass, on stones and hard roads. If they fail he fails. The feet should be wide and open, not narrow and contracted. If possible they should stand straight, and although a slight turn outwards is not detrimental, a turn inwards is. The latter will make a horse go close, and cut his joints. Lameness will soon arise in a horse with bad feet, and it is a point to which careful attention must be paid when buying. Many a man has had his eye filled by the symmetry and looks of a horse at an auction to such an extent that he has forgotten to look carefully at his feet, with the consequence that in a short time he has had no horse to ride.

"The other item, 'no hock, no hunter,' has a similar meaning. You see where the hocks are in your drawing. A hunter is subjected to severe trial by the nature of his work. Often the ground is deep and holding, when he is expected to jump and gallop with a big weight on his back.

"This he is not doing, like the steeplechaser, at a fast pace over clean fences, but frequently over stiff and awkward places which require him to jump off his hocks, getting all the power and leverage he possibly can from behind. The hocks are therefore put to tremendous strain, and if they are misshapen, small or weak, it won't be long before they break down.

"You may think I stress the hunter too much," continued Mr. Wisp, "but I can assure you that my only desire is not to advocate hunting, but to consider the horse at his most useful and hardest job to-day. The hunter, or at any rate the best of them, is either thoroughbred or nearly so. They spend many weary hours on the road travelling, have a weight on their backs all day, and are expected to stand still, gallop, or jump at any given minute.

"One might also say, 'No hock, no horse,' but it is the hunter and the steeplechaser to whom good sound hocks are more than necessary.

"A lump on the point of the hock is called a

' capped hock.' This is caused by the horse lying on it, or getting cast in the stable. It is a blemish, but not a serious one, and easy to see——"

" What does ' getting cast ' mean ? " inquired Jane.

" Getting down, rolling, and then losing his balance, so that he cannot get his legs beneath him to help him up. You may not think it possible, but it is. Sheep do the same thing.

" I am sometimes awakened in the night by a terrific kicking and horses neighing. I waste no time, for I know what it means—a cast horse ; and they can do themselves severe internal injury in their frantic struggles. I enter the stable as quickly as I can, and speak all the time gently in a level tone. If the horse is tied up I undo the ropes first. It is surprising how still he will lie, panting and heaving with distended nostrils, his appealing eyes watching me. I keep on talking to keep him quiet, and then take him by the head or tail and pull him over or round, and he gets up, with luck none the worse.

" They love rolling. A favourite hunter I had would lie down and roll immediately he got in his box after a day's hunting. If his rugs were only just thrown on loose to keep him warm, I'm blessed if he didn't manage to get up with them still on."

" Did he get capped hocks ? " questioned Miss Stuart.

" No, he was never cast whilst I had him. Another simple blemish of the hocks is curbs. These are not always on both hocks, but more often on one only. They are the result of a sprain to the ligaments at the back of the hock, situated five or six inches below the point. After treatment they become callus, and although not affecting his work, as a blemish detract from his sale value.

" On the reverse side of the diagram I have given

CAPPED HOCK   ---CURB

SPLINT------

you is a drawing showing a curb. There is one other blemish I want to explain, and then you will know the first step towards judging whether a horse's legs are clean and sound. This last is a splint.

" If you look at the drawing of this you will see that it is a slight enlargement on the front leg, on the inside just below the knee. It forms a little higher

73

sometimes, and also occasionally a little farther behind. Splints are formed as a result of concussion brought about by overworking or overweighting a young horse, or by a knock. They are bony deposits thrown out by, and to strengthen, the splint bones. These are small bones flanking the cannon bone.

" The inflammation of a splint is extremely painful, making a horse lame. As the splint hardens the pain lessens, and a fully developed splint never lames unless it interferes with a tendon or ligament on the lower part of the knee joint, to do which it would be higher than in my drawing. Splints are a blemish, but once formed can never be entirely removed, and, as I say, once developed do not usually cause any further trouble.

" I have now dealt with a capped hock, a curb, and a splint, and these will be enough external blemishes to tell you about to-day.

" In judging a horse's character look at his eyes and his ears. A full, bold eye, not showing any white, denotes courage, intelligence, and affection. An eye which shows white betrays vice, and a small eye, which we call a pig eye, indicates meanness. The small eye generally has a sullen look, and its possessor is sullen tempered accordingly. To hear some people talk you'd think all horses were angels, whereas really their characters differ enormously.

" The ears should be well shaped, of a medium length, and so give the head a sharp, keen expression. Give me the horse with the clean, small head,

74

bold eye, and sharp ears. Once you gain his affection he's your friend for life. He will rely on your judgment in his leaps, and trust you when his instinct warns him of danger. He will carry you as long as he has breath in his body, and respond to your moods of sorrow or joy."

Mr. Wisp paused and looked round at his small enthusiastic circle of listeners: John, leaning forward with his chin in his hands; Peter with his puckish little face, completely enthralled; Miss Stuart's eyes smiling approval, a pale gleam of sunshine through the window lighting a tendril of her fair hair; Miss Cushion shifting her weight slightly in her chair; Jane, alert and interested; Robin slowly absorbing what he heard; and Miss Allen's quick appreciative glance. Lucky Mr. Wisp to have the gift of making your subject so interesting! Lucky listeners to have so good a mentor!

There was a hoot at the gates, and a motor horse-box drove into the yard.

" Ah," said Mr. Wisp, " there's my new horse just arrived. Time we stretched our legs—eh, Miss Cushion ? Let's go to see him."

CHAPTER NINE

BLAZE ARRIVES—THE BRIDLE

THEY gathered round as the ramp was let down. Old Bob appeared with a halter and went into the box. The bars went up, the flap opened, and he came out leading a dark bay horse with a white blaze down his face. Freely and carefully he picked his way down the slope over the ribs of the ramp.

" What a beauty ! " said Jane.

Mr. Wisp turned to the driver. " I see he's fretted a bit," he said. "Hope you didn't come too fast ? "

" No, sir. I don't think he's done much travelling. But he didn't kick at all."

" Good. Pull his ears awhile when you get him in the stable, Bob."

" Right, sir. A nice hoss, sir."

" He'll make one. Walk him round the yard in the sun once or twice."

The horse followed quietly, throwing his head a little and looking keenly about him. He stood about fifteen hands two inches high, and moved with a long even stride.

" Do you notice how Bob leads him ? " asked Mr. Wisp. " From the near-side. The right hand on the rope near the jaw, the long rope end passing through his left hand. Should the horse jerk his head suddenly Bob's right hand might let go, but he would still have hold with his left. There, what did I tell you?"

The strange surroundings or the freedom after his recent confinement in the box caused the horse to suddenly jerk up his head, sniffing the air. He

gave a little squeal and stood on his hind legs, pawing with his fronts. Bob hung on the rope.

"Speak to him, speak to him," said Mr. Wisp, running over. "Whoa, my little beauty. There, now, what are you alarmed at, eh?"

The horse came down, and Mr. Wisp patted him, gently running his hand down his neck.

"Come on, my little beauty," said Bob, leading him on again.

" Keep on talking to him," said Mr. Wisp.

" What's his name ? " asked Peter.

" Blaze—from the white blaze on his face."

" How did you know he'd fretted ? " asked Miss Cushion.

" Because his ears were damp," replied Mr. Wisp. " That was why I told Bob to pull them when he goes in. It promotes circulation to pull the ears gently from the base towards the tip. If a horse's ears are dry and comfortable, soon the rest of his body will be also. There is less risk of catching cold too. He's only a baby, you know."

" Is he ? " said Miss Allen. " How old is he, then ? "

" Four years. He'll make a nice ladies' horse. Carry about twelve stone comfortably. One for you to ride later on, Jane."

" Oh, good ! "

" If you look at his head you'll see the sort I was talking about. Small, clean, and sharp. See how he pricks his ears ? How bold his eyes are, and yet how velvety soft ? He's settling down now. All right, Bob, put him in number four box.

" You should also notice how level and close to the ground he moves. Despite his long stride his feet hardly seem to leave it. That's another indication of a blood horse. If he lifted his feet high, with a bend at the knee, it would be a harness strain in his breeding, and make an uncomfortable rough gait, called high action. I don't deal in many horses, but those I do are worth the trouble and risk

78

involved. The worst of it is I sometimes find it hard to part with them.

" But this won't do. We must get on with our morning or it will be gone before we know where we are. Peter, please run and ask Darby to bring out Connie with a halter on, and the saddle and bridle spare."

Off ran the boy, and his young voice could be heard pealing out the instructions.

The sun now felt quite warm. Two or three white fan-tail pigeons flew about, whilst one kept guard on the pigeon-house platform, preening himself, strutting round with a bright eye on the cheerful group below. In a few minutes a stable door opened, and Darby's stocky form appeared, his close-cropped bullet head bare, and his red face grinning as he led the chestnut Connie out with one rug still on. He carried a saddle over one arm. Peter followed carrying a bridle, and they heard him saying, " I've found out where the cannon bone is, but I shan't tell *you*."

" Won't you," replied Darby. "Perhaps I know."

" No, you don't. You told me it was near the pistol joint, and a horse hasn't got a pistol joint."

" That was my little joke."

" It isn't a joke, then, it's a fib."

Conversing thus, they reached the others. Connie was a mare of the short, strong polo type. Keen enough when excited, but in reality of a very quiet, kind disposition, she was an ideal school horse, and soon became a pet with every one. She could stand any amount of work despite her nineteen years ; her legs were clean, except for one callus bump on the near hind joint, and her glossy coat showed her condition to be more than good.

"Now," said Mr. Wisp, "please pay careful attention as I want every one to-day to saddle and bridle his own horse. Before showing you the correct way to put them on I'll explain the different parts.

"Here's the bridle. This has two bits, and is commonly called a double bridle. The lower is the curb bit, and this is the curb chain. When the reins on this bit are pulled they tighten the grip of the chain on the jaw, and increase the pressure of the bit on the bars of the mouth, so you can see that it is not advisable to use this except as an extra aid. The other is the snaffle or bridoon bit, and should always be responsible for the most use. The ordinary snaffle bit, which, as you know, is used by itself, is naturally bigger and stronger than this one.

"The curb bit is divided into the mouthpiece and cheeks. Above the mouthpiece the cheek is called the upper arm, below it the lower arm. These two hooks are, of course, the curb-chain hooks, and this ring the lip-strap ring. The lip strap is used as a safety measure in case a hook breaks or the chain slips off. This semicircular lift in the mouthpiece is called the port.

"There are only six leather parts. The reins are obvious. This which passes over the head behind the ears is called the crownpiece, and this thin strap, which passes under the throat, the throat latch. The browband goes round the brow, the cheek pieces down the cheeks, the noseband over the nose, and there you are. Nearly everything is named by its approximate position or use. Now for putting it on.

" Take the bridle in the left hand by the crownpiece, and the reins in the right. Speak to your horse, ' Whoa, Connie, old lady,' and at the same time slip the reins over her head and down the neck, before removing the halter. This is done in case of accident. The horse might run back or turn round. With the halter still on, or without it with the reins on the neck, there is something to catch hold of.

" Slip the halter off. Stand close to the head and pass your right arm round under, taking hold of the crownpiece with the right hand and the bits with the left between the first two fingers, thumb outwards. Lift the right hand up, and put the off-side ear between the crownpiece and browband with a finger and thumb, at the same time inserting the left thumb in the side of the mouth. See how easily it opens, and the bits slip in ? Now get the other ear through, and it's on. I'll take it off, and let you put it on, Miss Allen."

" It looks easy enough," she said. " I suppose she won't bite me ? "

" Ha, ha ! " chirped Peter.

" Peter," mildly admonished Mr. Wisp, " remember everybody is not a fearless Indian warrior in his spare time—like you. Bless you, no, she won't bite. Put the thumb far enough back between the lips. There are no teeth there. Get the ear through first and the bridle won't slip down. Good. Now, Jane."

With the exception of Peter, who knew all about it, as he always put the bridle on the pony Tinker, each pupil tried in turn, on the whole with success. Miss Cushion, who was last, surprised them by her dexterity.

" I believe you've done it before," said Miss Allen.

" Indeed I haven't," she replied, blushing furiously ; " but I've always been quick with my hands."

" Well done," said Mr. Wisp. " Now for fastening. The throat latch first. This should not be too tight or too slack. In one case it would be uncomfortable, and in the other the bridle might come off if you fell over the horse's head. We hope that won't happen—eh, Miss Stuart ? "

" I thought I could rely on *you* not to show me up," she said.

" I scent mischief," said Jane. " Come on, be a sport and tell us."

" Well, if you must know, I was riding a horse from Eastbourne on the downs between Beachy

Head and Birling Gap. I put the horse at a small ditch, but instead of jumping it he stopped dead, ducked his head, and looked into it. I shot straight forward over his head, and the bridle came off. As I scrambled to my feet, he ran back, dodged me, and galloped home. I had to walk all the way back to Eastbourne carrying the bridle, and a nice fool I felt. When I told Mr. Wisp, he said it was my own fault for not checking the position of the throat

latch before I mounted. I admit he had taught me, as he's now teaching you, but in the excitement of riding a strange horse I forgot."

"You must have looked funny," said John. "But how do you check the right length, Mr. Wisp?"

"When the horse's head is up, the space should admit about three fingers—so. If you watch a good horseman mount a strange horse you will always see him check three things. The throat latch, the

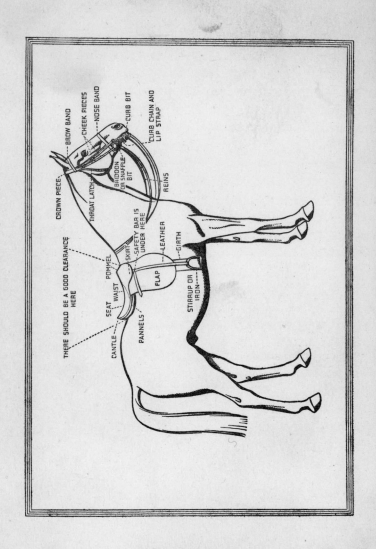

THERE SHOULD BE A GOOD CLEARANCE HERE

CROWN PIECE

BROW BAND

CHEEK PIECES

NOSE BAND

CURB BIT

CURB CHAIN AND LIP STRAP

THROAT LATCH

BRIDOON OR SNAFFLE BIT

REINS

SAFETY BAR IS UNDER HERE

SKIRT

POMMEL

SEAT

WAIST

FLAP

LEATHER

GIRTH

CANTLE

PANNELS

STIRRUP OR IRON

curb chain to see it's not too tight, and the tightness of the saddle girths.

" The noseband passes inside the cheek pieces, and should be comfortably tight. Its function is to keep the mouth shut. The curb chain should lie flat, and should be just tight enough to come up against this groove in the jaw when the reins pull the cheek pieces back to about forty-five degrees. The lip strap completes the job, and should be just tight enough not to slip below the lip, or your horse may get it in his mouth.

" When taking off, reverse the process. Undo the lip strap, curb chain, noseband, and, *last*, the throat latch. The latter should not be undone until your horse is safely in the stable. Of course, with Connie, who's so patient, we don't mind—do we, old girl ? " He slipped a piece of sugar in her mouth, and she gave him a look, one ear cocked as much as to say, " And about time too, old boy."

CHAPTER TEN

THE SADDLE—DARBY TAKES CHARGE

MR. WISP unbuckled the rug and folded it back over Connie's quarters. Taking the saddle from Darby and placing it gently in position, he continued :

" Before putting a saddle on, make sure the stirrups are run up the leathers, so that they don't fling against the horse or get caught on the stable sides. Also keep the girth over the top, and gently drop it when the saddle is in position.

" Always saddle from the off or right-hand side, as the girth is left fastened on this side, and place it gently down. In fitting see that there is a fair clearance in front and behind, because when the weight is in the saddle it may come down, and cause a sore wither in front or back behind. *Always* be sure of this clearance, and if ever you are in doubt, never hesitate to ask some one to look. Your forethought will be appreciated wherever the stable from which you hire. It may seem to you that the responsibility for this rests with the proprietor of the horse, and that as you are paying for the ride he should see to it. He should. But he cannot always be present, and when busy such things often go wrong. In reality, though, it is *your* duty as a horseman, both in the interests of the horse and yourself, to see that the saddle is properly fitted and comfortable. Heaven knows the number of people who get on a horse as if they were going for a ride on a bus, because they have never been properly grounded.

" Only the other day I saw a so-called riding master presumably giving a lesson. He was a length and a half in front of his pupil, one hand stuck on his hip, thinking of everything under the sun but the poor girl toiling along behind. Toiling she was, legs back, toes down, hanging on by her calves and the horse's mouth. The poor animal was as miserable as could be. He hung his head in shame at the exposure of ignorance in which he was an unwilling and helpless partner. If that was all the interest taken when she was mounted, you can imagine how little was taken before.

" So, as I say, check things over for yourself. The saddle then being in position, fasten the girths by lifting the saddle flap and fitting these tongues through the girth buckles. Do not pull too tight at once. You should be able to insert three fingers comfortably, and make a point of running them down to smooth out any wrinkles on the flesh.

" The parts of a saddle are few, its construction being built on what is called a tree. The front is called the pommel, the dip the waist, the back the cantle, and between the waist and the cantle comes the seat. The padded parts under these are called the panels and the rest are flaps, where your knees come, with the stirrup-leathers and stirrup-irons. This short flap covering the leather buckle is the skirt, and here is the safety bar. This latter should always be kept well oiled. In case of accident, such as a rider falling with a foot still in a stirrup, this bar will come down and allow the leather to slide out, or the unfortunate person might get dragged along by a startled horse. To prevent this you should also see that the iron is plenty big enough for your foot. Never ride with irons that fit tightly to your feet. Accidents are comparatively rare, and would not happen at all if little details like these were properly attended to. What are you grinning at, Darby ? You look like the Cheshire cat."

" I was just thinking, sir, how amused the ladies and gents would have been, especially Master Peter, if they'd seen Lord Falal at a meet of the hounds last winter. A great man he is for turning himself out proper. All scarlet and white, ye know, he looked a picture. Well, he goes to get on his horse without trying the girths first, puts his foot in the iron, gives a heave, and round comes the saddle, my lord and all, and down he sits in a proper squelch of mud. His language didn't make sense nohow. ' Darby,' he says, ' what the so-and-so are you laughing at ? ' ' I'm not laughing, me lord,' says I, ' I'm crying,' and I lost my job."

When the laughter had subsided, Mr. Wisp pulled a paper from his pocket saying :

" Now to work. Come with me to the harness room and we'll get your tackle."

They followed him to the well-kept tack room, where every saddle hung on its peg, the bridle below it, with each horse's name neatly labelled on the wall. Old Bob and Irish Jack were in attendance, and the latter, still dressed in his white stock and navy blue suit, paused in chewing his tobacco to say to Jane:

" 'Tis Goldflake you'll be riding, miss; and a

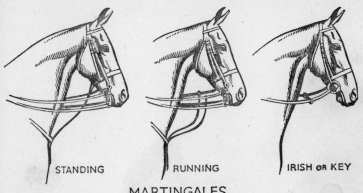

STANDING   RUNNING   IRISH ᴏʀ KEY

MARTINGALES

right good ride he is too. Helping you with the tackle I am, and a standing martingale all ready."

" Thank you, Jack," she replied. " I'm sure of getting it right with your help. But why the standing martingale ? "

" He carries his head rather too high for comfort; a trifle ' poky nosed ' or ' star gazing,' as we call it. The standing martingale, being the strap straight from the noseband to the girth, will keep his head more into his chest."

" Quite right," said Mr. Wisp, who had over-

89

heard them; " he goes quite well in that. It's a very common and ordinary safety check.

" Now, is everybody here ? Good. There are three men and myself to help you. When the tackle is on, place the curb rein under the stirrup-leathers, and bring the other over the horse's head, as I want you to lead your horses to the paddock. You will remember how Bob led Blaze—right hand close to the mouth, the length of rein in the left hand. The stirrups remain up, of course.

" Put the bridle on first, and then those whose horses stand in stalls turn them round before putting on the saddle. That prevents the risk of broken girths or saddle trees. John, you ride Prince ; here's the saddle and bridle. Jane, you ride Gold-flake ; Irish Jack will help you. Connie is for you, Miss Allen ; she's all ready. Robin, you've got Cocktail to-day ; and Miss Stuart will ride her own, of course. Peter rides Tinker——"

" Hurrah," broke in that imp.

" . . . and Ben for you, Miss Cushion. He's rather a big horse, so I'll come and help you. We'll have a running martingale on him as an extra check."

Great was the excitement and activity. Each one anxious to get everything perfect. Miss Allen having taken charge of Connie, Darby hurried to help John.

" Now there's no great rush, sir," said he, " and we'll be ready in no time at all. Put the saddle here. Good. Now speak to your horse. ' Get over, Prince, my beauty.' That's it. Undo the head collar."

90

John did as he was bid.

" Oh lawks, sir, don't let it drop on the ground ;
he might put his foot through it. Put it in the
manger. That's it. Now reins over his head. Speak
to him. ' Come on, my lad.' Got the ear through ?
Won't open his mouth, won't he ? Just move your

thumb up and down. That's done it. Now turn
him round. Good. Fasten the throat latch first. . . ."

John soon had that and the noseband fastened,
but rather fumbled with the curb chain.

" Let me show you," said Darby. " Twist it
to the right and it will come flat. Hook the end on
first, and then the adjusting link ; the third one
down will be about right. Look at this noseband.

That won't do. The Guv'nor 'll have a fit if he sees that. You've put it outside the off cheek strap instead of inside."

John refitted it, saying :

" Careless of me. Comes of being too anxious."

" That's all right, sir," replied his guide, grinning away ; " do no worse than that and you won't hurt. To take his rugs off, undo this roller first, and place it over the stall partition behind you. Then unfasten the rugs in front, and pull them off over his tail in as clean a sweep as you can. That keeps the coat down. The rugs should be neatly laid over the stall partition, same as the roller. Now for the saddle. Before you fasten the girths nip round to the other side and make sure the under flaps lie smooth. They sometimes ruck up."

" They're flat enough," said John. " I don't pull the girths up quite tight yet, do I ? "

" No, just tight enough. He's like most hosses. Blows himself up with wind, so that when you get on his back he lets it out and the girths are then too slack. Just tighten them right up in the paddock before you mount. He'll lose the air in walking round there. Try the length of the stirrups."

John did this by putting the finger points of his right hand under the buckle on the saddle, and, pulling the iron to the full extent of the leather with his left hand, tested whether the iron reached his armpit. It was short by two inches.

" Too short," said he, and proceeded to adjust it by pulling up the spare end of leather and lengthening by two holes. He did the same the other side, tucking the spare end under, pointing to the rear. He then remembered Mr. Wisp's instructions, and ran the irons up the leathers to the top, placing the curb rein under them, and pulling  the snaffle rein over the horse's head. He was now ready.

Mr. Wisp came along.

" Everything all right, John ? The others are ready." He ran his eye over the horse, feeling curb chain, throat latch, and girths. "Good. Out you go, then."

CHAPTER ELEVEN

THE PADDOCK

ONE entered the paddock by gates leading from the yard. It lay behind the stables and was beautifully situated for its purpose, being some two hundred yards long by seventy-five to one hundred yards across. At no little expense and trouble Mr. Wisp had made a cinder-track right round it, which also crossing in the centre made the figure eight. At one end, fifty yards long by four yards deep, was a roofed shelter. The posts supporting this were twelve in number, and had the double advantage of being used for bending practice, as well as with the addition of sheep hurdles making a splendid jumping lane, which allowed a jumping lesson even in wet weather. Situated on the wall in the centre was a large mirror, in which a pupil could see himself, thereby enabling him to correct his faults unaided.

The various poles and fences were neatly arranged together near the shelter, waiting their turn. Here were none of the so-called permanent fences so often found in riding establishments, with pieces knocked out of them, and the ground—after countless lessons—rutty and uneven for take-off or landing.

Mr. Wisp fully understood the value of giving his

94

pupils confidence, and knew that this object would be entirely defeated if the horses they rode were asked to jump on bad ground. Many a keen beginner has had permanently shaken nerves through lack of attention to such small details.

As this day's pupils filed past, Mr. Wisp took his stand just inside the gate. In place of the pleasant, smiling look his grey eyes had when lecturing, was a direct eagle glance noting the smallest detail. He was like the captain of a ship as he leaves the river mouth and touches the open sea. The file, almost needless to say, was led by Peter with the mouse-coloured pony, Tinker. " Stop it," said he, as that keen animal laid its ears back and kicked out at Jane, who followed, leading the bright chestnut, Goldflake.

" Don't go too close, Jane," called out Mr. Wisp. " Keep a clear horse's length behind. Don't pull down so hard with your right hand. Feel the bit, but don't weigh it down. Peter, lead the way right round once."

He knew that a walk round would stretch their legs, and minimize the trouble from freshness.

Miss Stuart's horse was a bright bay blood—a typical ladies' hack, clean and elegant. He pranced a little with excitement, and Mr. Wisp thought what a lovely picture they made, as with a healthy glow in her cheek and a sparkle in her eye she restrained his impetuosity.

Prince—" the Black Prince," as Peter called him —was going kindly with John, as was also the sedate grey Cocktail with Robin. Miss Cushion came next, with " Big Ben," another of Peter's christenings (learnt from Darby), and the rear was brought up by Miss Allen with Connie. Each horse looked in good condition, ready and fit for work. They were good school horses, and even Goldflake, who was slightly excitable, or " gassy," as some people term it, knew his work and soon settled down to it. Mr. Wisp walked round with them.

" When I say, ' Halt,' " said he, " stop, and turn your horses in, facing me ; and whether riding or leading them, remember to keep at least a horse's length behind the one in front. Halt ! "

The order was obeyed.

" Now," he continued, " see that the girths are tight enough. John, I can see Prince's will go up a hole or two. Replace the reins over the head and pull down the irons. Miss Cushion, the next order does not apply to you. Every one ready ? When I say, ' Prepare to mount,' turn your back to the horse's head, place the reins in the left hand, and place your left foot in the stirrup. When I say, ' Mount,' do so, and turn your horses to the left. Prepare to mount. Mount. Good. Robin, you must be quicker next time. Now, Miss Cushion, I'll give you a leg up. Place the reins in your left hand and face the horse. Bend the left leg from the knee and place it in my hand. When I count three spring from the other foot. One, two, three, up you go ! *Don't* look down to fit the right foot in the iron—feel for it. Got it ? Fine. . . .

"You'll go round in single file, and from time to time I want you each to take the lead. So increase your horse's pace by extra slight nagging pressure of the calves and legs, keeping a fairly short rein, but don't pass too close to the others. Peter, you keep the lead for the time being. Walk on.

"Miss Allen, your stirrups are one hole too long. Don't take your foot out of the stirrup to adjust them. Pull out the loose end of the leather, press down with the foot, feeling for the next hole with your thumb. That's right. *Don't* look down, do it by feeling. Jane, ease your rein a little more, and loosen the curb rein. That horse needs riding on the snaffle. John, straighten your back more. No, not as if you'd swallowed a poker—naturally. That's better. Look straight in front of you."

As they neared the stacked fences, Ben began to sidle away from them.

"Miss Cushion," said Mr. Wisp, "move the rein which is farthest from the fences. Move it about to distract your horse's attention, and speak to him, then he'll think of you and not of them. Don't move it too much. See the difference it makes? The same applies to you, Robin. Always remember that. If a horse is inclined to shy at anything, call his attention from it with the farther rein and your voice. . . . When I give the order, 'Prepare to trot,' shorten your reins. Prepare to trot! Trot! A steady, collected trot, please, Peter."

They trotted round, at first with a little disorder; but the horses knew the curriculum, and soon every

one was going well, Mr. Wisp telling one person
to keep the elbows in, another to keep the hands
lower and to loosen the wrists. After two circuits
Mr. Wisp called to John :

"John, take the lead. Trot your horse on faster.
Urge him on with your legs, but keep a short hold
of his head to keep him trotting. That's good.
Now ease your rein slightly and steady him up to
the former pace."

Jane's turn for the lead came next, then Robin's,
and so on, until every one in turn had "trotted out."
"Walk," called Mr. Wisp. "Next time round
thread the posts at the top. As you incline your
horse to the left, use your left rein and right leg;
incline to the right, the right rein and the left leg.
The leg thus prevents your horse from swinging
out his quarters."

The movement was performed at the walk and
then at the trot. "Walk again," was the next
order.

"The next pace will be the canter," said Mr.
Wisp. "It is to be done, as I've taught you all
individually, from the walk. Shorten your reins,
slightly increase the pace, turning the horse's head
a little to the left, increase the pressure of both legs,
but use the left leg more strongly. This will mildly
overbalance your horse to the right, and make him
lead with the off fore and off hind legs to save himself. If he doesn't go at once, then apply your left
heel sharply. If any horse goes on the wrong
leg, you'll soon know by his uncomfortable gait.

Is that quite clear ? Prepare to canter. . . .
Canter !

"Miss Cushion, your horse is on the wrong leg.
Pull him up and start again. . . . That's better.
Not too fast in front, please. John, take the lead.
Send your horse on ; now steady him. . . ."

The orders were given in a drawn-out manner,
such as W-a-l-k, which gave every one time to do it
slowly. Mr. Wisp then set them going in the
opposite direction. The time simply flew. After
twenty minutes, walking, trotting, and cantering,
making the complete circuit, and with variations
round the figure of eight, Mr. Wisp halted them.
Each one turned in, facing him. "Now pat your
horses and speak to them," said he. "They've
earned two minutes' rest. The next movement is for
you to walk round, with the stirrups crossed on your
saddle front, and I'm going to call you each out in
turn to criticize the others—take my place, in fact.
Just glance at yourselves as you pass the mirror,
and then you'll see yourself as others see you."

This idea was a great success. John, who had
recently visited an army school with his uncle,
properly imitated a riding-school instructor, directing the majority of his remarks to his sister.

"You on the chestnut horse," he shouted, " sit
up, can't you ? Keep your hands lower, you're not
writing a letter home to father. Why is your horse
prancing ? Make him walk. You ought to be on
a donkey." This last remark was more than sisterly
flesh could stand, and much to every one's delight

99

she called back : " One donkey in the class is enough."

And when her turn came she fairly criticized every one in turn except John, whom she dismissed with, " The handsome young man on the black horse rides too, too beautifully."

" He does," said Mr. Wisp, smiling at her, " but look whose brother he is. H-a-l-t, please. Miss Cushion, will you come here with me for a moment ? Thank you."

He turned to the others. " Now, with your stirrups still crossed in front of the saddle, I want you to trot. Miss Stuart, will you please take the lead, and start at a gentle trot—what I call a ' hound trot '—so that every one will not rise in the saddle, but will sit still. Remember that the secret of riding without stirrups is to keep your feet and legs in exactly the same position as if the irons were still in use. I shall then ask you to increase the pace to a normal trot, when you will grip well with the knees and rise to the bump in the usual way. Walk on, please."

Miss Stuart led as requested, and when the order to trot was given set a five-mile-an-hour jog. The pace was increased to the normal trot, and they rose and fell in the usual way, every one finding it surprisingly easy. Before they could get tired Mr. Wisp ordered the walk, and then gave the order to resume the stirrups.

" What a relief to take the stirrups again," thought Jane, for Goldflake was somewhat inclined to bounce about. It was great fun nevertheless; she had never realized before how jolly a school lesson could be.

Mr. Wisp had the knack of making the work interesting, knowing full well the value of variety, and how necessary it is not to overdo the thing. So that no one should feel too fatigued he gave them frequent rests. Any one who is keen enough will go on and on, doing as they are told in the school, and it is only afterwards that they feel fatigued, for there is no doubt that riding makes a strenuous call on many little-used muscles, and if the full enjoyment is to be obtained strain must be avoided.

Mr. Wisp next dismounted Robin, Jane, John, and Miss Allen, saying that it would do them good to change horses, and for each person to adjust his own stirrup lengths. Robin changed to Connie and Miss Allen to Cocktail, whilst Jane exchanged with John, he getting on Goldflake and she on Prince. The four of them went round the school by themselves at a slow walk, a fast walk, a slow trot, a fast trot, then a walk, and, last, a canter.

Miss Cushion, Peter, and Miss Stuart remained in the centre with the instructor. John was heavier handed than Jane, and had a little more difficulty in restraining Goldflake, until Mr. Wisp called him in and tied up the curb rein, leaving it looped loosely on the horse's neck. He then went more easily.

At the end of ten minutes Mr. Wisp called them

into the centre, halted them, and told them to pat and speak to their horses, whilst he sent Miss Stuart, Peter, and Miss Cushion off on a similar journey, but giving them a shorter time.

Miss Cushion got on very well, considering she was the least experienced, only showing a tendency to look down instead of straight forward between her horse's ears. Mr. Wisp had his own method of dealing with that, however.

" Have you lost anything, Miss Cushion ? " he called out.

" No," she replied. " Why ? "

" Oh, nothing," he said, " only you give us the impression that you have, as you keep looking down. If you aren't looking for anything please keep your head up, chin in, and look to the front. That's better."

All being assembled in line again, he put them through several useful exercises, the stirrups being crossed once more in front of the saddles. First to relax and sit loosely, letting the toes drop, then to raise the toes and sit and grip correctly. Next, swinging the legs backwards and forwards from the knee, keeping the rest of the body still.

" For exercise three," said Mr. Wisp, " will you please place your hands on your hips, and throughout all the exercises look straight to the front. All hands on hips ? Good. When I say ' one,' swing the body forward; ' two,' come back upright; and at ' three,' swing the body back, returning to the upright on ' four.' One—two—three—Miss Cushion, you can

EXERCISES

go back farther than that—don't move your legs, Robin, keep them in the correct riding position—four. Now again. One—two—three—four. One—two—three—four. Jane, you hollow your back too much. Once again. One—two—three—four. Thank you. Relax and rest for a moment."

Turning the body to left and right, both while sitting down and standing in the irons, was the next exercise, hands on hips; and lastly they finished with each arm in turn upward stretched, then down to touch the opposite toe, the hands returning to the rein position between each movement.

" Pat and speak to your horses," said Mr. Wisp, he himself giving Goldflake a caress. " To finish the lesson we'll have a little jumping—shall we, Peter ? "

" Oh yes, please," replied his lordship, the picture of smiling impudence on the pert Tinker; and looking up at Miss Cushion, towering above him on the redoubtable Ben, he naïvely said, " If Miss Cushion's not too tired ? "

" Not a bit of it," the lady replied; " but I've not done any jumping yet, and don't think I'm ready for it. Am I, Mr. Wisp ? "

" Well, not quite," he said. " I intend to start you in a week or so by yourself, without an audience.

" Whilst the men are fitting the wings, all dismount, please, and loosen the girths two holes. Get down quietly, John," said Mr. Wisp as he walked off to superintend Darby and Old Bob, who were getting the fences and wings ready near the shed.

" I say, Jane," said John, " it was pretty mean of you to call me beautiful."

" It was mean of you to shout at me," she answered.

" I was only pulling your leg," he said. " You ought to see what those army chaps go through. That instructor the other night looked as if he ate live coals for breakfast."

" Ha, ha ! " chirped in Peter, " I saw a man the other day who swallows swords—whole ones. You saw him too; didn't you, Robin ? "

" Yes, at the circus. But he can only take one at a time."

" Well, I should think the chap I saw eats *buckets* of live coals," said John, not to be outdone.

CHAPTER TWELVE

JUMPING

"WHAT'S that about eating live coals?" asked Mr. Wisp, returning to the paddock from the jumps in time to hear John's remark.

"John was talking about the army instructor he saw the other day," explained Jane.

"He must have been one of the old school," said Mr. Wisp, "or else he had an exasperating lot of recruits. In the old days the instructors were almost inhuman. Thank goodness a little common sense has been introduced into riding instruction instead of brutality. I've seen men absolutely raw during their first few weeks in the cavalry, so that it became agony for them to sit on a horse. It just shook their nerves, so that only by dint of much bullying, and suffering on their part, they eventually became soldiers capable of riding on parade, but very rarely horsemen. The horses knew the routine backwards, and obeyed the word of command by themselves. A visit to the Military Tournament at Olympia will soon show you the difference which exists to-day. Do you ever go?"

"Yes, I went last year," said Miss Stuart, joining the little group.

"Then you saw a very fine exhibition of training in horse and rider," continued Mr. Wisp.

"What did they do?" asked John.

"I'll tell you more about it when we've more time," he replied, "but in one event there were

three large banks which the horses jumped on and off many times, and then finally three of them jumped on, stood still, and lay down on the bank, just at the word of command, with the rider still on. That's something like training. There was another horse which jumped, one after the other, a line of six swords stuck in the ground. No wings or anything as a guide except the man on him. A very fine display, don't you agree, Miss Stuart ? "

" I certainly do," she replied. " Perhaps this year we could make up a party and take some of the youngsters. It would be such fun to go with you as a guide."

" Good idea," said John. "What about it, Jane?"

" Rather ! "

" Me too," said Peter.

" Of course," said Mr. Wisp. " Thank you for the compliment, Miss Stuart. Now to work once more."

Raising his voice to attract the attention of Miss Cushion and Miss Allen, who were chatting apart, he said : " Some of you have done a little jumping before, but as this is a class lesson I shall treat you all alike and keep the lesson simple. As Miss Cushion is not jumping, you will ride Ben, John ; Miss Allen will return to Connie, and Robin to Cocktail, whilst Miss Vanster will continue with Prince. Goldflake is a little too excitable.

" I shall fasten a spare stirrup-leather round the neck of each horse for you to hold on to, as when learning to jump every one automatically jabs his horse in the mouth in order to keep his balance. This develops bad hands, and is hard on the horse.

" The first secrets of jumping are grip, balance, and the ability of the rider to swing his body in time with his horse. I shall therefore ask you not to hold on to your reins, but to hold on to the neck strap. There is no danger of the horses running away, because they are all good school horses, and will follow each other well. There are three fences in the lane, the first two are poles and the third is a small brush fence. You will find they are low, so that you will hardly notice the horse jump.

"Concentrate on keeping your legs still, and slightly lean forward as you approach each obstacle. The horse will swing you back, and leaning forward a little will enable you to counteract the backward thrust. Miss Stuart, you are the most experienced person here, so will you take the lead, please, and when ready set a nice steady canter."

The exchange of horses being made and the girths tightened, they mounted and rode round at a walk first, to get the correct distance of three lengths between each this time.

Mr. Wisp had fitted the neck straps, and now walked round with his pupils.

Although they had all done a little jumping before, they still experienced that inward feeling of excitement which nearly every one has at the prospect of coming face to face with obstacles which have to be negotiated.

As they walked along, Mr. Wisp admonished them on no account to try to help the horse to jump, but to leave it to him, saying that there was no risk of a fall, and in any case no horse foaled would fall if he could save himself by jumping. His final orders were :

"Miss Stuart, canter round the paddock after the last fence and then walk. Every one else is to set his pace by Miss Stuart's. I shall get you to canter one at a time, and as you approach the fences I want you to lower the hands and hold on to the neck strap, leaving the reins loose. After the last fence shorten up your reins again.

"Are you ready ? Robin, just glance down and put your feet a little more forward. Right. Canter, please, Miss Stuart. Canter, Miss Vanster—now, John—off you go, Miss Allen—same for you now, Robin. Steady, Peter, now you can go."

Miss Stuart set a nice steady pace. As Mr. Wisp had told them, the horses were all good school horses, and knew the pace and work required of them, so that they all negotiated the fences without incident, and with the minimum of effort on the part of the riders—the mousy Tinker popping over the fences with his ears pricked, Peter sitting like a limpet on his back, his eyes alight with excitement.

Three times they jumped the course in this way, and then Mr. Wisp advanced the work a little by giving them two turns with the stirrups crossed in front of the saddle. He then halted them, saying, " Pat your horses and speak to them, and rest for a minute. The next thing is for you to go one at a time, by yourselves, with your arms folded, but retaining your stirrups.

" It would be better for you, Miss Allen, if you leant forward a little more as you approach the obstacles. You are rather inclined to be left behind your horse. Robin, next time try to grip a little more with your knees, and keep your toes up more. You were hanging on too much with your calves, and not gripping in enough with the knee. John, there is no need to wear such a grim expression; Ben is a lovely jumper, isn't he ? "

" Rather," said John; " but he feels a bit on the big side."

" Well," said Mr. Wisp, " that should make the fences look smaller. By the way, I hope you've noticed the whistling noise he makes ? You can see it doesn't distress him, but it's there all the same. Are you satisfied about that, Miss Cushion ? "

" Oh, yes," she answered. She was holding Goldflake, and had been an interested observer whilst the others jumped.

" Right, that's good," he said, and calling Darby, told him to raise the first pole one notch and the second pole two notches.

" That will make the horses jump a little higher," he explained, " and will give you more chance to swing with them. Miss Stuart, will you go first and show them how to do it ? "

She walked her horse to within fifteen yards or so of the first fence, then set him into a canter, dropped her reins, folded her arms, and away she went. One, two, three, a really good show, sitting perfectly.

" That's the way to do it ! " exclaimed Mr. Wisp. " Now, John, walk your horse to the same place. Off you go."

The redoubtable Ben cocked his ears, and

jumped truly and well, like the old hunter that he was. John put up a good effort ; he lost his balance slightly at the second fence, but the next one came so soon that the horse righted him. Jane went next. She was naturally graceful, and found no difficulty in adapting her body to vigorous movement. Miss Allen and Robin followed. Peter would not be denied his turn, but Mr. Wisp would not allow him to fold his arms, making him use the neck strap as previously.

They each had three turns, improving with each one, and Mr. Wisp was just telling them how pleased he was when the entrance gate opened and in rode the popular Mr. Carew, looking the epitome of a good horseman on the gay, intelligent Peppermint.

He was neatly dressed in a tweed jacket, bowler hat, collar and tie, fawn breeches, and black boots. His shoulders were slightly rounded, with the elbows in and the hands low, the backs of them being parallel with the horse's shoulders. His feet were level, and right home in the irons. He seemed to be part of the horse, so well did he sit, and his body swung gracefully to the horse's swinging walk. Peppermint had his ears well pricked, and moved with a long, close-to-the-ground stride. He made a beautiful and unusual touch of colour in the wintry sunlight, his deep crushed-strawberry coat gleaming, thrown into contrast with his dark points.

" Good-morning, everybody," called out Mr. Carew, raising his hat. " Thought you wouldn't mind if I joined the lesson, Mr. Wisp ? "

"Not a bit of it," replied that worthy, his kind face lighting to a smile; "jolly glad to have you. It'll do the little horse good, and perhaps you'll oblige the company with a little song and dance?"

"Not to-day, thank you," replied his friend; "my voice is breaking, and goes up and down the scale like a cuckoo with gout. Besides, Peppermint objects to discords—don't you, old boy?" he asked, patting him affectionately on the neck. "But joking apart," he continued, "the horse does look well; really does you credit. Don't you think so, Miss Stuart?"

"I certainly do," she answered with a look that showed her interest in the questioner.

"Mr. Wisp," piped up young Peter, "could Mr. Carew show us how to jump?"

"If he will," replied Mr. Wisp. "What about it, James? Our lesson is just over, and it would be most helpful if you'd give a little demonstration."

"What do you want me to do?"

"Well, that little horse is pretty handy now. I'd like you to walk and trot collected, and to walk and trot out, to change legs at the canter, get him on the wrong leg and put him back, and by that time he'll be warm enough to jump. Will you do it?"

"As we're amongst friends I will. It will give you a chance of explaining things to them of which I suspect you to be ignorant yourself. Although I don't want to disturb their faith in you, O mighty Wisp! Come on, Peppermint, and don't *you* expose me, old chap."

"Thank you, James Impudence," said Mr. Wisp; "off you go. What fences do you want?"

"Hurdles first, bush fence next, and the gate, fairly low, last," he called back over his shoulder.

"What did he mean when he asked Peppermint not to expose him?" asked Jane.

"His theory is," replied Mr. Wisp, "and it's mine too, that it is easy for a horse to expose the faults in his rider by behaving in an unexpected manner. We developed it as a joke at first, but there's quite a lot of truth in it, although you may not appreciate it for some time yet. Now watch."

CHAPTER THIRTEEN

PEPPERMINT'S DISPLAY

CAREFULLY watched by his eager audience, Carew was gently walking Peppermint down the track when they neared the entrance gates, which were shut. He began to sidle towards them, and suddenly without warning stood straight on his hind legs. Without turning a hair the rider leant his body forward, easing the reins, and then, poised as they were, brought his heels back sharply into Peppermint's ribs.

" I expected that," said Mr. Wisp with a nod as the onlookers held their breath; " but James knows what he's up to. See how quiet he is, talking to the rascal all the time. He'll settle in a minute. A time when one needs a firm seat and a cool head. Ah, he's going again now."

" Why does he do that ? " asked Miss Cushion. " I hope one never does it with me. I should die of fright."

" So should I," said Miss Allen.

" Pooh," said Peter, " I should hit him."

" And that's just where you'd be wrong, young man," said Mr. Wisp; " especially with that horse.

together by the rider. You should also note how neat and tidy James looks. I don't mean in dress only, but in general appearance. His elbows are not stuck out, with the hands held high, which is a style very much in vogue at the moment amongst a lot of people who've reached the stage where they are perfectly at home on a horse, and which, apart from looking ugly, really throws the muscular action on the stomach instead of the shoulders.

" No ; his elbows are close to his sides, but not tightly so, and his hands low. He grips with his knees and his calves, but not the back of the calves, because that would throw the knees away from the saddle instead of into it.

" As he turns to the left, his right leg and heel keep the horse's quarters from swinging to the right, which would unbalance him. You can see this well at the walk, although it is done of course at all paces.

" Do you notice, Miss Cushion, how he looks straight to the front, between the horse's ears ? His mind is working with his horse, anticipating the next move. At the first sign of anything alarming he will speak to him, calm him and soothe him with his voice, establishing a confidence which can only exist between a horse and his rider.

" As he trots the same tidiness remains. The whole body in time to the horse, gently and quietly. What a grand swinging stride that horse has got ! I'm sorry I sold him."

" Well, then, try to buy him back," said John.

Mr. Wisp cocked an eye at him.

" John," said he, " a bargain's a bargain. Apart from the ethic principle of such an act, it is entirely against the grain of a horse dealer."

" Sorry I spoke," said John.

" Don't apologize," said Mr. Wisp. " But he's going to make a grand horse. He's so well balanced."

" What does that mean exactly ? " asked Jane.

" The horse carries himself so well, with his head in the right place, and his legs moving so truly, that he can execute any movement with the greatest of ease to himself and his rider."

Carew eased the horse to a walk and stopped near them.

" Do you want me to rein back ? " he asked.

" You may as well," replied Mr. Wisp, " but we haven't reached that yet. We have our work cut out to go forward, don't we ? "

" We do," said Miss Allen; "but we should like to see it."

" Right, then," said the demonstrator, " I'll do it here. All I do is this. Feel his mouth gently with the reins as an indication of what I want, and lean my body a little forward. As he steps back, I relax the reins and keep the pressure of my legs even, to keep him collected. He goes back in a straight line, with his head held fairly high. When he halts he does so standing properly on all four legs. If I were not talking to you at the same time, which prevents me from doing so, I should say ' B-a-c-k ' to him with each step. I do it so that

in time he will associate the word with the movement, and will only require the merest indication
of the order. He's an intelligent animal. Aren't
you, old chap?" he asked, patting him. "Come on,
we'll warm up with a canter."

He walked the horse forward a few paces, and
struck him into a canter, in the way in which Mr.
Wisp had taught them, from a walk.

"He does ride beautifully," said Miss Stuart;
"don't you think so, Jane?"

"Rather," she agreed; "it all looks so easy the
way he does it."

"That is the art which conceals art," said Mr.
Wisp. "He rides exactly as I described when talking to you. He's a bold, quiet, and skilful horseman.
You must remember that he's been doing it for some
years, with a great many opportunities which a great
many people never get. But please don't let it dis-
hearten you, or I shall be sorry I asked him to ride
for you. Cheer up," and he looked round at them,
his kind eyes smiling.

Carew was cantering round the lower circle, and
as he came towards them on the right diagonal,
Mr. Wisp took advantage of it to point out the value
of the horse leading with the correct foreleg according to the direction in which he was travelling,
pointing out that the horse was going well balanced
and "true." That is to say, he was leading with the
off foreleg, followed by the off hind.

"Going incorrectly now," called out Carew,
and he changed the leading foreleg to the near fore.

The change in the horse's comfort was immediately apparent, even to the inexperienced eyes of the small audience. Mr. Wisp explained that this action was called "Cantering false." Carew kept Peppermint on the wrong leg until he turned to the left in the circle near them, and then called out, "Strange as it may seem, he's now going true again. Marvellous, isn't it? Eh, you boys?" with a wink at Peter and John as he passed by.

"Doesn't the off-side foreleg become the near-side foreleg when that comes nearest to you?" said Miss Cushion.

"Good gracious, no," said Mr. Wisp; "the off-side is the right-hand side, and the near-side the left hand. They never change whichever side you are. If you want to know how to remember it, think on which side of the road you drive. Which side is that, Peter?"

"The near-side, of course," said he, with an expression which clearly said, "How can any one be so stupid," so that Mr. Wisp said, in order to check his tendency to scoff at Miss Cushion, "What about France?"

That stumped him, especially when Miss Cushion, the kindly soul, replied for him:

"In France they must drive on the off-side, then."

Mr. Wisp affectionately brushed up the ends of his neat grey moustache.

"Here he comes," said Robin. "I want to see him jump."

" So do I," said Jane.

" Now, ladies and gentlemen," said Carew in the best circus manner, " you are about to witness with your own eyes something the world has never seen before. An insurmountable obstacle jumped by an unjumpable quadruped, ridden by a two-legged ass. Sound the trumpet, please, Peter."

" Ta-ra-ta-ta-tah ! " went Peter, entering into the fun of the thing and making a trumpet of his hands.

" Steady, old boy," said the horseman as the horse snorted and bounded on seeing the fences in front of him. He kept talking quietly to the horse, which was impatient to go, endeavouring to walk him to within a few lengths of the first fence. Reaching the desired spot, he let him go, restraining his pace so that the horse would jump off his hocks. Even the imperturbable Mr. Wisp was excited, and entirely unable to resist pointing out how well his friend tackled the job.

" See how he throws the weight of his body forward from the waist and thighs," he exclaimed, " the short distance that he gives before starting. How quiet, but how determined he is, with his eyes looking forward over the fence. The obstacles are not big, but it is just as necessary to be determined to clear them as if they were twice the size."

Peppermint cleared the first hurdle with a tremendous bound, dropped in a short stride at the brush fence, just flicking through the top twigs, and cleared the gate with a foot to spare.

"Well done, my lad," said the rider, patting him and pulling him up to a walk.

"Put the gate up a bit, please, Darby," he called out, "and put a pole along the top of the brush."

"Yes, sir," said Darby, all alive; "mind he doesn't jump the whole shed next time, sir." He did as he was bid, muttering to himself, "That hoss has got wings."

The performance was repeated, Carew never moving in the saddle, except to give the horse "the office" to take off at the bigger obstacles. This giving "the office," as it is called, can only be done by the experienced horseman, and is really a part of his determination to clear an obstacle. It would probably lead to disaster if attempted by a beginner, as it will force a horse to a mistake unless given at exactly the right moment. There was thus a difference between Mr. Wisp's way of teaching and Carew's performance, which the former was careful to tell them in as simple a way as he could.

"As you progress," he said, "I shall teach you to jump bigger obstacles, in which you will have to judge the distance from which to start, and the pace at which to travel. Then you will have to be determined to clear them, and will give your horse 'the office' to take off, as Mr. Carew did just now. The best distance for a horse to take off is the same as the height of the fence he is about to jump. Thus if a fence is four feet high he should leave the ground four feet before it. This ensures a good

" Amen to that," said Mr. Wisp. " What do you propose to have for lunch ? "

" Half a dozen oysters, brown bread and butter, and a glass of ' bubbly.' I've one or two rough races in front of me shortly. Will you come ? You can have what you like, and the pudding will keep."

" I should love to," replied Mr. Wisp as they entered the yard, where the men were busy washing the horses' feet. " What are you doing, Robin ? " he said to Robin Briscoe as that youth came forward carrying a bucket of water and a water brush.

" I'm just going to wash my horse's feet," he replied, " as there are two horses to every man, and I should like to know how to do it."

" Good for you," said Mr. Wisp. " Let's see you start."

Robin put down the bucket beside the horse, and taking from it the brush full of water, began to brush the near forefoot vigorously towards himself. In a second his jodhpurs were splashed with dirty water.

" Just a moment," said Mr. Wisp; " look what a mess you're making of yourself. First of all take the brush full of water and dab it several times on each hoof. That will soften the dirt. Then fill the brush full of water again and brush it round the hoof, but down towards the ground. The splashes will then go on to the ground, and not on you. In doing the front feet place the disengaged hand in front on the knee to stop the horse striking. When you do the hinds, place a hand on the hock, in the same hand also catching the tail, if the horse has one, and so prevent him kicking. Don't walk round the horse, but work all the time from the off-side. The feet should be picked up and washed out inside, and then you'll be able to see if any stone has lodged there. Run the hand down the leg to the joint, facing the tail of the horse, then grip the joint and place your elbow in the back of his knee, press with

it, and up will come his foot. Then wash down into the bucket. I'll show you how to pick up the hind feet."

"Gracious," said his pupil, "I never realized there was all that in it."

"There's a lot in the correct way to do everything," replied Mr. Wisp. "Go on, I'll help you."

Robin set to, Mr. Wisp directing each operation, and when the turn came to wash out the hind feet, he showed him how to pick them up by getting hold of the joint from the inside, explaining that if it were done from the outside, and the horse kicked, he would run the risk of a broken arm. He next told Robin to get a leather and dry the heels, saying how susceptible to cracks, or chaps, the heels were in the winter unless properly dried.

The horse had had his feet washed so many times that he almost picked them up before asked to do so, which was a good thing as it made Robin's first experience of a groom's work all the lighter.

" I say," he said, as John strolled up to watch him, " have you ever done this ? "

" No," said John ; " it doesn't look difficult, though."

" It isn't," said Robin, " but there's more in it than meets the eye. You try it."

The effect on John recalls that famous occasion when Tom Sawyer got his friends to paint the fence. John immediately wanted to do the job himself, and off he went to persuade Darby to let him do Prince.

Mr. Wisp smiled, and winked at Carew.

" Now you'll mess up them nice trousers, sir," said Darby.

" No I won't," said John ; " Robin hasn't." At a sign from Mr. Wisp, Darby gave in, and John began operations.

" Bless me, sir, forgive me for contradicting of ye, but just look at ye," said the groom as John splashed himself. And so his lesson started.

Irish Jack, chewing tobacco as usual, came and

washed Peppermint's feet and took him to his box, followed by Mr. Wisp and the owner. Jane came in with some sugar for him.

"He's a darling, Mr. Carew," she said. "I do wish I could ride him."

"If you go on as you are doing," said he, "I'll give you a ride on him shortly."

"Really, do you mean it?"

"I never say things I don't mean. I think you are progressing splendidly."

Jane's eyes shone with pleasure, and a lovely tinge of red came into her beautiful young face. The horse rubbed his head against her, and she covered her confusion by kissing his velvet muzzle.

"Come with me," said Mr. Wisp, "and we'll get his food."

They went together to the zinc cornbin at the end of the stable.

"Peppermint is in fairly hard condition," said Mr. Wisp. "He's hunting now, and has some hard work to do. We therefore give him two measures of whole oats "—putting it into the sieve held by Jane, "one and a third measures of bran, and a double handful of chaff. That's it."

As she entered the box the horse stamped and kicked, lashing his tail with excitement.

"Speak to him," said Carew, "and come wide of his heels. He doesn't mean any harm. He's only ready for it. Lots of blood horses are like that."

"All right, all right, my beauty, I'm coming," said Jane, tipping the food into the manger.

" Mix it well with both hands," said Mr. Wisp ; " it's most necessary to promote good digestion."

She did so. Peppermint snorted into it and settled down, stamping now and again. Jane patted him affectionately.

" I must find John," she said. " We must run home to lunch. It's been a lovely morning, Mr. Wisp."

" Good," he replied. " It's more routine work this afternoon. Don't be late back, will you ? "

" No fear," she replied. " I expect I shall find John with Darby."

" We must be off too," said Mr. Wisp. " I'll just cast my eye through the stables, and then I'm ready, James."

" Right ; I'll go and start the car."

CHAPTER FIFTEEN

GROOMING

THE stables and yard lay basking in the mild sunlight, with that peculiar look that indefinably marks the early afternoon. A stillness held everything in peace.

Even the white pigeons were still on the platform of their cote, chests tucked out and heads tucked in, an occasional coo alone breaking the silence. A relic of old England was this quiet little haven, tucked away in the outskirts of a great and roaring metropolis. Here the hand of time went back. Back to the days when man depended for his sport and means of travel solely on four-footed friends. Back to days of leisure, space, and beauty. Lucky is the man who, pausing in the excited turmoil of the present day, can appreciate this peace. No wonder so many people are returning to the horse for their pleasure.

So thought Mr. Wisp as he stood at his door surveying the scene, relishing a five-minute pipe before his pupils returned. He had enjoyed his lunch, and as they were back in good time, Carew had shot off like a rocket to give Jane and John a surprise lift in his car.

They were the first to arrive.

" That was grand," said Jane as she got out of the open sports car, tucking the windswept tendrils of hair back under her hat.

" Hullo, Mr. Wisp," said John; " are we the first to arrive ? "

" You were," replied he; " but here come Robin and Peter. I hope you didn't drive fast, James ? "

" I *know* he did," said Peter, joining them. " I saw him. Flashed past they did, and Jane was laughing."

" Well, you know what the Arabs say," said Carew; " ' the grave of the horseman is always open.' "

" I should amend that," said Mr. Wisp, " to ' the grave of the motorist never shuts.' More applicable in my opinion."

He smiled quizzically and went on :

" You look a lot fatter, Peter. Hope you haven't eaten too much, or you'll be incapacitated by stitch."

" I haven't,"replied Peter; " they won't let me. But Robin has."

" I haven't," indignantly answered that young man; " you were the more out of breath."

"Well, I was galloping. I always gallop."

"It's a bad thing to gallop between meals," said Carew solemnly. "A horseman like you should know better."

Peter looked puzzled, so Jane spoke up for him.

"Mr. Carew's only teasing you, Peter. Here come Miss Allen and Miss Cushion."

"I can see *she's* been galloping," said the irrepressible imp, who went everywhere imagining himself to be a horse. The latest arrivals were followed by Miss Stuart in her car, and in a few minutes the class was once again complete.

"Off we go to the stables," said Mr. Wisp. "It's a case of 'coats off and braces down' this afternoon. As you'll never groom a horse, James, even were I able to teach you, we'll leave you to your own devices. Will you give Blaze, the new horse, a turn in the paddock, and let me know what you think of him?"

"With pleasure," replied his friend. "Any dodge to look out for?"

"No; he's quite genuine. Too honest to be a rogue."

"Good. I shall enjoy myself. Mind you people take what he says with a grain of salt."

"We will," they chorused as they followed Mr. Wisp to the stables.

"Good fellow, James," said Mr. Wisp to Miss Stuart; "he loves his little joke."

"I shouldn't describe you as lacking in humour,"

she replied, and frankly added, " I think he's charming."

Mr. Wisp smiled and gave his moustache a gentle flip at each end.

Darby opened the door for them, and as they entered they encountered the lovely clean smell of a well-kept stable. Mr. Wisp was very particular about the litter on which his horses stood, not begrudging the few extra shillings a week it cost to keep it perfectly sweet and clean. He was justly scathing in his indictment of establishments where they were not so particular, letting their animals stand on damp and sodden straw or peat in order to save so small a sum. He regarded the practice as offensive to the horses, to the clients, and altogether as false economy.

" Now then, Darby," said he, " have you got the tools ready ? "

" I have, sir," replied Darby; " they're just by Prince."

" Remember to pick up your feet," said Mr. Wisp, leading the way to Prince's stall. " I'm going to let Darby do a little talking, and show you the right way to groom or ' strap ' a horse. When he's shown you, those of you who want to can each do a horse. How about you, Miss Cushion ? "

" I'd love to try," replied the lady. "A little strenuous exercise will do me good."

" Right.   Carry on, Darby."

That gentleman had his braces down, his red face was wreathed in smiles, the blue eyes looked sharper than ever ; he was the picture of cherubic activity.

"Now then, ladies and gents," said he, "the first thing we've to consider is the tools. This stiff brush is called a 'dandy.' I uses that first to get the dirt off. A dandy is a useful brush, and can be used for doing dogs as well as hosses, and also can be very handy in the home for clothes. I always keeps one myself for that purpose.

"The next brush is this one with soft bristles called a 'water brush,' and this one with a strap

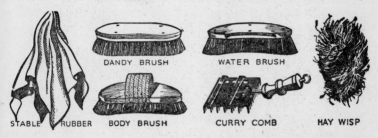

STABLE RUBBER   DANDY BRUSH   WATER BRUSH   BODY BRUSH   CURRY COMB   HAY WISP

on the back for my hand to go through is a 'body brush.' That fetches out the scurf, dust, and grease, and as I use it I continually draw it across this currycomb, which in turn fetches the dirt out of the brush.

"This here is a 'wisp,' which we make ourselves out of hay, and it's used for putting on a polish. This cloth is called a 'stable rubber,' and is used for finishing off.

"When an hoss is rugged up in the winter, you don't strip him out until you're ready to use the body brush. You turn the rugs back from the

quarters over the shoulders and start on the quarters
first with the dandy. Start the off-side, and work
like this with your hand working behind you. In
other words, you use the brush with the right hand
for the off-side and the left hand for the near-side.

You brushes and works vigorously, hissing to keep
the dust out of your mouth."

He suited the action to the words, hissing and
working away. " I shan't spend as long on the job
as I ought," he continued with a grin, " or you'll
be bored and want to run off and play. As I works
down the thigh, please note I put my left hand on his
hock to prevent him kicking, and I keep my hand
there all the time I'm doing his leg. You'll also see

I work towards his tail, and where he's dirty I uses a circular movement, but finishing the stroke the way his coat lies. Next comes his tail, which wants well brushing.

" Moving round to the near-side, I go forward to the edge of the rugs and work backwards again, same as before."

" Why do you work backwards ? " asked John.

" Why ? Because then you're working the way an hoss's coat lies, and can get more power in your arm.

" Having finished his quarters, hind legs, and tail with the dandy, you then repeats the process with the water brush, this time only working the one way, and with the brush damp, not wet. To get the brush damp you put it in the water and then draw it sharply across the edge of the bucket, pushing it away from you so that it splashes into the bucket. Like this. It's a funny thing, but most people new to the game draw the brush towards them first off and get soaked." Darby talked as he worked, and soon finished the quarters.

" There, my beauty," he said, drawing the turned rugs back in place.

" Now we looses the hoss and turns him round. Mind your backs, please. Come on, Prince."

He undid the head collar and the patient Prince, knowing what was expected of him, turned round.

" If he doesn't turn round freely of his own accord, just get hold of his ear and lead him round by it. An ear's a very useful article. Hearing's not the only use it has—eh, Master Peter ? "

" You can't box a horse's ears," said Peter, seeing the point.

" Why, bless you, no," said Darby, " but you can lead him by one. I now unbuckle the rugs in front, and turn them back over his quarters. Starting with the dandy on the off-side once more, I go over his head, down his neck and mane, shoulders, chest, front leg, withers, back, and girth. Both sides as before, and then with the water brush. You'll notice I keep a hand on his knee this time, to prevent him lifting his foot or striking. Then sponge out his nostrils and eyes." They all watched carefully, admiring the skilful way he worked.

" Some hosses are more thin-skinned than others," continued Darby, " especially bloods. They can't stand the dandy, and you have to be careful, sometimes not using it at all. It's then a case of elbow grease, elbow grease all the way. In racing stables the dirt comes out of them easily, because they sweat well at work and are groomed twice a day. It does an hoss good to sweat well, although as ye know, you should always cool him off before you bring him in.

" We had a gent here a few weeks ago who brought an hoss in hot. It was a treat to hear the Guv'nor tick him off. Quite a stranger he was. Asked him if he'd won his race! ' What race ? ' says the gent. ' What! ' says the Guv'nor, ' you haven't been racing? Then how in the so-and-so has your hoss got so hot ? Pardon my curiosity,' he says in his quiet way, ' but where did you learn to ride ? ' ' Oh,

in different places,' says the gent. '*In*different places,'
says Mr. Wisp. 'Come into my office before you
go, if you please.'"

" Has he been again ? " asked Miss Allen.

" Oh yes, he's been again. Very tactful, is the
Guv'nor. Can't afford to lose custom, you know.
Can't afford lame hosses, neither. That gent now
thinks the Guv'nor's a trump. He'll make an hoss-
man some day—*if* he lives to be a hundred. Well,
there we are. Dandy and water brush used. Now
we turns the hoss round, puts on his head collar,
and fastens him up on the rack chain. Off with the
rugs, in a clean sweep over his tail, and placing them
neatly—neatly, mark you—on the stall partition.
Now, starting off-side once more from the head, we
works like a nigger with the body brush, scraping
it from time to time on the currycomb, and tapping
that article on the floor to empty it."

The horse's coat began to gleam under the
expert manipulation of the body brush and the
strong arm wielding it. The amount of dirt which
came out was surprising.

" I could spend a long time on this job," said
Darby, working with a circular and then coatwise
movement, " but I can't. There isn't much to say
about it, for it's elbow grease that does it. Did
ye ever hear the tale of the two fellows who rode
every Sunday morning ? A ' weekly liver shaker,'
they called it. They came from opposite directions,
and met in the middle of the morning at a certain
pub for a welcome half-pint. One day only one

fellow turned up. He waited a long time for his pal, who failed to come at all. The next week they met as usual. ' Where did you get to last week ? ' says one. ' I came the same way as usual.' ' Ah, yes,' says t'other, ' but *I* had a different hoss ! ' "

When the quiet chuckle this little joke evoked had subsided, Miss Cushion asked why the horse's head was racked up on so short a rein.

" Well, ma'am," said the groom, " I don't suppose as you'd be very keen on having a piece nipped out of you. We always tie 'em up tight so as to be able to really work at 'em with the body brush. Hosses is sometimes ticklish creatures, and apt to give one a playful nip. They don't mean any harm, but what's a playful nip for him can be a painful one for you. It doesn't hurt the hoss to be fastened like that, of course.

" Talking of hurting hosses I remember a cruel instance "—he gave John and Peter a violent wink as he said this. " Two friends had been for a ride, and afterwards each had taken his own hoss into its box, and the boxes were next each other. Suddenly Mr. A starts shouting and swearing something awful. B rushes from his box to find A's hoss standing on his foot and refusing to budge. ' What's all the noise ? ' says B. ' Can't you see he's on my foot ? ' says A, and B callously replies, ' I can't see what all the fuss is about. It's not hurting him, is it ? ' Well, the next day they were again in the stable, when B starts to shout and swear, and on running to his assistance A discovers B in the same predicament that he himself was in on the previous day. Looking as solemn as an owl, he says, 'What's all the row about ? ' ' The so-and-so's on my foot,' says B. 'Well, well,' says A, ' it's not hurting him, is it ? ' "

Darby paused to look at his audience, his face beaming to see his joke appreciated. It was even more so when Miss Cushion said with a puzzled look, " I don't quite see that. How could the horses be hurt ? "

" Now, ma'am," said the groom with a waggish grin, " you mustn't pull my leg. I'd better get on with the wisp before you asks me any awkward questions. The wisp is made of soft hay, and, by vigorous usage in the same direction as the coat lies, will produce a gleam and shine. It's a satisfactory article to use, for it soon shows its work. It's only human nature to like to see the fruits of one's labour. There's a shine for you ! " he exclaimed as after a few minutes' vigorous application the horse's coat began to shine. Darby only spent a few minutes with the wisp, as otherwise his audience would have wasted time watching him.

He finished off with a clean stable rubber, finally sponging the dock out just as Mr. Wisp arrived.

" Well," said he, " what sort of an instructor is Darby ? "

" Fine," said Jane; "he has amused us, the horse, and himself."

" Do you think you know any more about strapping now, John ? Miss Allen ? "

" Rather," said John; " I want to have a go."

" So do I," said Miss Allen.

" Off you go, then. The men will give you the tools. You do Bob, the cob ; and you can do Connie, Miss Allen. Any more for the fatigue party ? "

" Yes, please," replied the others.

So Jane went to do a horse named Sailor, which she had ridden several times ; Robin was allotted Cocktail, Peter claimed Tinker as his right, and Miss Stuart her own horse Oriflame.

" I'll come with you," Mr. Wisp said to Miss Cushion. " We'll tackle the bay mare at the far end. She's very quiet."

Darby could be heard explaining things to John, and Irish Jack devoted his attention to Jane.

" Don't forget to speak to your horses frequently," called out Mr. Wisp. " Treat them as friends and associates. Keep your voice quiet and level in tone."

CHAPTER SIXTEEN

JOHN TAKES A HAND

NEARLY an hour passed very rapidly for the amateur grooms, who certainly found it much harder work than it looked. Mr. Wisp walked round from time to time, correcting a fault with Robin or giving extra explanations to Miss Allen or Miss Cushion. They all felt very warm, and one or two in their hearts felt thankful they didn't have to do it every day. Mr. Wisp watched John replace the rugs on Bob. As he was buckling the roller Mr. Wisp said :

" I believe you've forgotten something, John."

" Have I ? " said John. " I've tried to remember everything Darby told me."

" Do you see how tightly that roller fits to the horse's back ? It must have had a pad under it. I expect it's in the straw."

John settled into a steady even turn. It went surprisingly easily at first, but after four minutes began
to seem like work, especially when Bob was using
the knife where the hair was thick. John stuck it,
however, his whole body breaking out in a gentle
sweat, but was glad to stop when the old fellow told
him to.

" You have a cut at it, Robin," said John.

" Not such easy work as it looks, eh, sir ? " said
David.

" No," said John; " that's the second time I've
been disillusioned this afternoon."

" What a man," said Jane mockingly, turning to
Miss Allen and Miss Stuart, who had just arrived;
" John finds that hard work."

" Well, you try," said John. " I didn't say it
was *hard* work, but it's not so easy as it looks, that's
all."

Robin began to turn. Bob was clipping the head,
the legs and body being already finished.

" Here, David," said he, " come and hold his
ear. . . . When I was with the Lady Sarah we had
nothing but hackney show horses, and fine big 'uns
they were too. Some of 'em stood seventeen hands,
and they wanted some clipping I can tell ye. That
was before the days of even this machine, and we
had to shave 'em with a razor.

" When this machine came in we had a job to get
the horses used to the noise. You see, if a man
makes a mistake with the knife he gives the horse
a nip, and ever afterwards the animal associates the

146

pain of that nip with the noise of the machine. I remember we had a hackney stallion which got a nip the first time he was done. Did he carry on afterwards ? A lion at feeding time was like a dove compared to him."

" Then how did they manage to do him ? " said Miss Stuart.

" Well, it took four men. We put a twitch on him first. They aren't really allowed now by the R.S.P.C.A., but a lot of people still use them. It's a piece of cord on the end of a stout stick about a foot and a half or two feet long. You put the loop of the cord over his top lip, and then turn the stick until the cord's very tight. It can then be held, or else fastened to the top of the head collar. It may be painful, but it keeps a horse quiet. With this customer we put the twitch on, and fastened it to one ear. Then a man held up a foreleg; mind you, he was racked up as well, because the first time he threw himself down and injured the man holding his leg. Even then he'd make a fight of it, and doing him always took us a day. Easy, sir, have a rest."

Robin stopped turning and straightened his back, saying, " You were quite right, John. We'd soon get muscles like the blacksmith if we did much clipping."

" Let me try," said Peter, who had been watching everything, and was now walking round Old Bob, and peering closely at every turn of his gnarled hands, " I'd like muscles ' strong as iron bands.' May I have a turn, Bob ? "

" Not to-day, sir. But you can run and ask
Darby to give you the tapers. I'll finish off his head
with a singe."

" If the twitch is forbidden, it must prove that
it could be done without," said Jane. " Is there any
other remedy for a fractious horse ? "

" The Guv'nor favours the Comanche twitch,"
replied Bob, " because it can be used only when
necessary. You fasten a cord to the upper D of a
head collar on the near-side, then pass it over the
poll and down the off cheek, bring it round here,
just above the teeth on the upper gum, under the
lip, up the near-side cheek, and through the D of
the head collar again, leaving the end loose. A
man holds the end and pulls if he needs to."

Peter now returned with a wax taper, and Old
Bob lit it, running the flame rapidly round the jaws
and then the ears, flicking it up and down, and rub-
bing out the burning ends of hair, whilst David
held one ear to keep the head low, and with his
hand shaded each eye in turn.

When finished the head looked very clean and
sharp.

" There you are, my beauty," said Old Bob.
" Now where's that resin, boy, and I'll just pull this
tail a bit."

David produced a tin of resin, into which Bob
dipped his fingers, and, taking a small steel comb
from his pocket, began rapidly pulling and shortening the hairs at the top of the horse's tail.

" Why do you use resin ? " asked John.

" To help my fingers to grip. I'm going to thin this hair out at the top for about ten inches down, then put a dry bandage on it overnight. Makes a graceful tail. We had an hoss here a short time since who'd come from one of those places where they have cheap labour, as the Guv'nor calls it. Some one there had put a wet bandage on his tail, and put it on tight, too. The poor wretch was blistered underneath where there's no hair, and it took him weeks to get right. Where's that tail bandage, David ? "

" Here you are," said the lad ; " and here's the water brush to damp the hair first."

" Learning, you are," said Old Bob, and catching sight of Mr. Wisp, continued, " Just finished, sir. Hope the company's been entertained."

" It's feeding time," said Mr. Wisp. " Would you people like to help ? "

" Yes, please," was the unanimous answer.

Mr. Wisp divided them into three parties, one for each stable. Jane, John, and Peter went with him to number one stable ; Miss Stuart and Miss Allen to number two, under Darby ; and Miss Cushion with Robin to number three, under Irish Jack.

The horses stamped and kicked the boards as Mr. Wisp lifted back the cornbin lid.

" They know the time," said Jane.

" Yes ; and the noise," said Peter, calling to his pony Tinker, who was nickering in his nostrils as well, and making enough noise for one three times his size, " All right, Tinker ; I'm coming."

" I like to hear it in preference to all your modern

music," said Mr. Wisp. " It shows the horses are fit and well when they're anxious for their food. Now, John, fill this sieve for Prince ; one-and-half measures of corn, the same of bran, and fill up with chaff. Speak to him as you go up to him, and go up the off-side. Mix it well in the manger with both hands. Go with him, Peter, and bring back the sieve whilst he's mixing the food."

" Do they always have it so dry? " said Jane; " it seems most unappetising."

" Well, it does them more good to have it dry, at least for getting them into hard condition, but we do damp it several times a week. Every Saturday night they have hot linseed with it, and I also give them molasses in liquid form. Both foods are good for the coat and greasing the insides, helping digestion by lining the stomach.

" If I buy a thin horse in poor condition I spend some weeks in carefully feeding him; and do not expect to see him put any flesh on outside for some time as the inside has to be well lined first. Thank you, Peter—take that to Tinker."

John returned, saying to Jane, " You ought to see old Prince stuffing it; fairly snorts. You'd think he hadn't had a feed for weeks."

" Mr. Wisp says that's as it should be," she answered. " Somewhat reminiscent of my dear brother tackling chicken."

Mr. Wisp smiled to himself.

" Maybe," said John, hastily dropping the subject. " Where next, Mr. Wisp ? "

" The brown mare Polly, next to Prince ; there you are."

" I gave Tinker a knob of sugar as well," said Peter. " He nearly ate my hand too."

" Hard luck," said Mr. Wisp. " Now take this to Silver, and mind she doesn't nip you."

Chatting and joking, the feeding was soon done, and the three pupils waited for Mr. Wisp to give them the next move. Taking a bottle of methylated spirits from a shelf, he said :

" Polly has a slight sprain on her near foreleg, so I'm going to put on some methylated spirit to keep it cold. It's wonderfully cooling, and doesn't harm the skin or coat."

They watched him rub on the lotion gently. "Fancy methylated doing good," said John. " Do you use it anywhere else ? "

" Yes, we do," answered Mr. Wisp, who thoroughly enjoyed himself with these three pupils, because they asked such intelligent questions and were so keen to learn. " Methylated is very good for hardening horses' backs. When they come in off grass in the autumn their backs are easily bruised after being so long without a weight on them. Methylated is an economical method, and has saved me many pounds.

"In the case of strained legs we also put the hose-pipe on them, often for hours at a stretch. The cold water has just the same effect as it would have on your own wrist or ankle. Peter, are there four bandages by Prince's stall ? "

" Yes, there are."

" Bandages are also a help in supporting a horse's legs, which have to stand up to much hard work, and yet are so delicately constructed. There are two separate methods of putting on bandages. For night, we bandage from below the knee, down over the joint, and for travelling we stop just above the joint. The bandages must be on much more tightly for travelling, and in both cases the cotton wool must be clean and lie flat, or else it will pinch and mark the hair in rings.

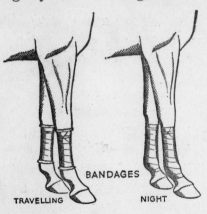

BANDAGES

TRAVELLING   NIGHT

" Watch me put them on Prince for the night. Notice that I work from the off-side, and bind the bandage away from me. I start here, on the cannon bone, work downwards right over the joint, back up again, and end neatly just below the knee. In tying the tapes I use a reef knot, and then tuck the ends well in round the tape. Do you know why, Peter ? "

" So that the horse can't bite them and pull it undone. Irish Jack told me that. He said that one morning in Ireland he found a horse dead. During the night it had worked its bandage loose and then been frightened through constantly treading on it. Do you think it did really happen, Mr. Wisp ? "

" Well, Peter, it sounds rather far-fetched, but at the same time it is possible for accidents to happen. One must always remember to expect the unexpected with horses. A little carelessness can cause a lot of harm. Supposing you put on the next one, Jane, as you ought to be fairly deft with those nice hands."

" Well, I'll try," she said. . . . And made a very good job of it too.

Mr. Carew unobtrusively joined them, and stood quietly watching Jane perform.

" Nicely done, young lady," he said as she finished and rose. " By the way, Will, what about asking these people in to the ' sanctum ' for a cup of tea ? "

" With pleasure," answered Mr. Wisp. " I had thought of it, but we can't accommodate them all."

" Of course not, but I've made arrangements to be in the chair for *this* little party. I suppose your lesson for the day is nearly over ? "

" Yes, it is. You take your guests along, and I'll just say good-night to the others, and see that everything's all right. I'll join you in ten minutes or so."

" What about it, young Peter," said Carew; " can you toy with a cream bun ? "

" I should just say I could. But we must watch that John doesn't make his ears sticky, mustn't we, Jane ? "

" Enough of that, young 'un," said John, grinning good-naturedly. " We're game, aren't we, Jane ? "

153

" I should love a cup of tea," she answered.

" Come on, then "—and off they went, leaving Mr. Wisp to finish bandaging Prince. He watched them go with a pleased and slightly quizzical expression on his kindly face.

CHAPTER SEVENTEEN

FIRESIDE CHAT

IT was dusk as they crossed the yard, and when their host switched on the light in the " sanctum," as he called it, the room presented a very cheerful sight. The guests were somewhat familiar with it by now, but it never waned in fascinating charm for them. A cheerful fire blazed in the hearth, and the friendly copper kettle was in his usual place, awaiting his turn to serve his pal the teapot. The table was laid with cups for five, complete with two silver dishes laden with the most appetising-looking cakes and a plate of thin bread and butter.

" My word," said Jane, " who cut such beautifully thin bread and butter ? "

" The hand which trembleth not, neither doth it lie," said Carew, striking a melodramatic attitude.

" Meaning ? " she persisted.

" Your humble servant," he said with a bow.

" You ought to have been a cook," said John.

" No, a nactor," said Peter.

" There, you see," said Carew, " to such depths are the mighty fallen. ' A cook,' says one, ' a nactor,' says the other. A horseman never."

" I should say one needs good hands for all three," remarked Jane.

" Young woman, you say sooth and restore my self-respect. Do you know what that thing is ? " he said, turning to John, who was examining a new sheepskin numnah lying on a chair.

" No, I don't," said John. " It's a new one on me."

" That, my tyro, is a sheepskin numnah, to go underneath the saddle on my redoubtable Peppermint's back. I've just had it made to fit my saddle. You can feel how soft it is, and easily reason that it eases the pressure on a horse's back, especially when he's thin-skinned like that rascal. I hope Mr. Wisp has not neglected to tell you how important is the fit of a saddle ? "

" He explained that this morning, and has actually told us about it on other occasions," said Jane.

" Some people use a felt numnah," continued Carew, " but I prefer a sheepskin. The only point is that sheepskins must be kept soft by washing and brushing well. They save many a back from being sore."

" Sookie's singing," interrupted Peter. "Hurrah, here's Mr. Wisp," as the master entered the door, exclaiming, " By Jove, it looks cosy in here. Did I hear the kettle singing ? Then we'll have tea. Milk, sugar, everybody ? James, do the honours with your own provisions. Gracious, what a rich assortment of cakes ! "

" Yes," replied his friend, " I told the girl they were for *you*. Peter, you're the most active member of the field, so please hand round the bread and butter. My father always said that no man would be sick on cream if first he had a good foundation of bread and butter. I suppose you've been told that before now ? "

" I always have to eat two pieces at home," said Peter with a sad air, politely offering the plate to Jane.

" How did the horse behave, James ? " asked Mr. Wisp. " I've had such a busy day I'd *almost* forgotten that you'd been on him."

" Very well. He's a little bit green, but as you said, much too honest to do anything wrong. He'll come on well with a few weeks' nagging to keep him up to his bridle."

"Nagging," said John; "that's a peculiar expression. I thought only wives nagged their husbands."

" What a cynical thought," said Mr. Wisp. " Nagging means working at a horse to make him fully collected. That is, working with the legs, hands, and body. There are men called professional nagsmen who do nothing else. They are employed by breeders of horses and assist in breaking in. When a horse is ' broken,' it simply means that he is quiet to put a saddle and bridle on, quiet to sit on, and has learned that he is in the service of man. After that he has to be taught manners. To stand still for the rider to mount or dismount, to walk at five miles an hour, to carry his head well, and generally to proceed in all his paces in a collected manner. Young horses do the most disconcerting things—eh, James ? "

" What things ? " asked Jane.

" Go on, James," said Mr. Wisp ; " you tell them. They must be fed up with my lectures to-day. I'll have another cup of tea, please, Jane."

" Well, you're much more competent to tell them than I am," said James, " but as we're all friends together I'll try to explain what you find so difficult to say. Have you ever observed a baby learning to walk ? Seen how he stumbles and tries to save himself ? How sometimes he sits down unexpectedly, and sometimes when he was walking splendidly stops dead-still to listen. So it is with a young horse. He will stop suddenly and even refuse to go a step farther. Under pressure to do so from the rider he will refuse, and resort to obvious methods of showing his disapproval, such as rearing or turning round in circles. He may even duck his head and kick out behind."

" How nerve racking," said Jane. " I don't think we appreciate what well-mannered horses we ride."

" ' Appreciate ' is the right word," said Mr. Wisp. " Few people who take up riding for pleasure appreciate the training the horse has had to enable them to ride him at all."

" Now who's telling this tale," said his friend ; " you or I ? "

" Sorry," said Mr. Wisp. " I forgot it was your stage."

" You're a born moralist," admonished Carew. " Try one of these chocolate·éclairs, John. The girl in the confectioner's assured me they contained real cream. Let's see, where was I ? Oh yes, stopping, et cetera. . . . Well, at times like those it needs a very firm seat, and a lot of determination and patience to prevent an open fight. Should it come to that, it might happen that the horse would win. That's what happened to our friend Peppermint, for instance ; he evidently discovered that by rearing he could frighten the man on him into getting off. The logical result would be that one had a useless horse, capable of making a fool of one at any moment he chose."

" Unless he met his match in some one else," said John.

" Just so. But he must do that while he's still young enough to learn. Good nagsmen earn the same money as bad ones, and that's not much, the only difference being that they keep their jobs longer.

" Going back to the baby simile for a moment, one finds in horses just the same incompetence to control their movements, and even in human beings one sees people who would have walked a good deal straighter, or carried their heads better, or been less round-shouldered or bandy, if they'd had a good nagsman of a nurse instead of a bad one. Rather an amusing idea that, Wisp. Let's start a Nagsmen's

Crèche. 'Wisp & Carew, Ltd. Babies taught correct carriage at all paces.'"

"No thanks," said Mr. Wisp; "I'll stick to horses. They don't talk so much. Have another cake, Peter."

"What else do horses do ?" asked Jane. "I used to think they carried people naturally as soon as they were old enough to bear the weight. Shows how ignorant one can be."

"How much they do," replied Carew, "or for how long they do it, depends entirely upon each horse's character and temperament. Most of them do nothing vicious at all, and only need teaching collection, whilst others will buck, or lie down and roll, or try to rub the rider's leg against a wall or any other object that's handy. Some will 'fly jump'— that's a leap of some yards forward from the hocks entirely without warning, usually followed by a violent plunge of the head and a bolt.

"Mr. Wisp had one of that sort once, and asked me to ride him. We were going along beautifully, and I was just thinking to myself that they'd given him a bad reference without justification, when, without the least intimation, he leapt to one side, clearing a flight of iron railings at one bound."

"What on earth did you do ?" said Jane, her eyes expressing the horror of her imagination.

"Sat quiet and as tight as I knew how. He was past curing, and Mr. Wisp did the best thing by cutting his loss and selling him for a third of what he gave for him. But the worst sort of all are those which run backwards, because for that I don't believe there is a cure. I thought I'd be very clever once, and bought an astonishingly good-looking horse for a song without knowing his 'If.' I soon found it out when he crossed a field backwards with me nearly as quickly as he could go forwards, then turned round and did it the other way. But I'm telling you more about confirmed rogues than about the disconcerting tricks of young horses.

" Some people think that if a horse develops vice it has been put there by man. In many cases this is true, but in some it isn't, because the vice is hereditary and incurable. There are criminal horses just as there are criminal human beings, and even with the best and kindest handling possible, the bad will out. One always likes to think that one will be the chosen person to whom a cunning horse will respond kindly, but I've only found it so once or twice. Don't you agree, Will ? "

" I certainly do," said Mr. Wisp, his pipe in full blast. " The only thing we can say is that every type of horse teaches you something, and the man who has ridden many learns to understand the equine mentality, and develops a sixth sense, which is very closely allied to the horse he is on. . . .

" James, you omitted to tell your audience about the excitement a young horse shows in his first day or two out hunting, and the awkward way in which he tackles his fences. How he wants to tear at full gallop after hounds, and how he will jump at some fences with feet to spare, and get so close to others that it doesn't seem possible that he will be able to jump at all. Times when the nagsman has to be prepared for a fall, and yet not let the horse know he expects it for fear he shakes his confidence. Times when the nagsman sits tight and collects his horse from a bad peck on landing or gives him a lift over a ditch on the take off. A bold man with an eye for a country, and a quiet way with him, can make a hunter in a few days to hounds."

As he spoke Mr. Wisp's eyes lit up reminiscently, recalling many a scene of flashing excitement. Keen as he was on hunting, he never tried to influence any of his pupils, realizing that in most cases they would never do it, and that his duty lay in teaching them how to obtain the maximum comfort and enjoyment from ordinary riding, without favour or prejudice.

" I should like to hunt," said Peter.

" So should I," said John.

" I shouldn't," said Jane. " To me it seems so terribly cruel."

" That's a discussion into which I never enter," said Mr. Wisp. " Not because I'm afraid to, but because there's a lot to be said on both sides. The only thing I can say is that I've seen some of the most beautiful sights of my life when following hounds. Glorious views, and views which one could have seen without hunting, but then they would not have seemed the same without the quick excitement and colour of the chase.

" I remember one very windy day, when the wind blew so hard that one was almost deafened, we ran from a plain up the downs. I ascended to the top, and after running along this for some way the fox set his mask for the plain again. As I came down a precipitous slope, some hundreds of feet below me hounds were running, and the sun shot out in a long shaft of light from between the clouds, lighting the swift-running pack into a gleaming flash of pied purple and white on a sea of green. The open grey sea itself was on my right, and inland the woods lay dark and moaning. It was a rare moment as I felt myself suspended between heaven and earth, the horse beneath me feeling for his every foothold as we descended.

" The light often plays queer tricks with the colours of hounds. I've seen them appear to be of a liquid deep blue; and I remember one day in a grass country I was well away in front of the field, and as the huntsman and I landed over the first fence into the adjoining field the light seemed to change into a peculiar limpid green, and the huntsman and hounds looked for all the world as if they were in very translucent water. At such times one entirely forgets the quarry and is completely carried away by the beauty and excitement of the scene."

He paused, and for a few minutes there was dead silence, each one busily conjuring his words into mental pictures of their own. Peter started the ball rolling again in a different direction.

" John says he's going to have some breeches and boots for a birthday present."

" You will later on," said Mr. Wisp. " You'll enjoy it, John; and it's packed with information, most of it just as true to-day as when it was written years ago. I'll come and see you safely off the premises."

" I'll run them home," said Carew, " and come back for a few minutes' chat. That will give you a chance to make up your slate for to-morrow."

" Good idea. Well, good-night, Jane; good-night, John. Have you got your muffler, Peter; you'll need it in that car ? Draughty thing."

" Yes, thank you. Good-bye, Mr. Wisp. Mind you give Tinker that piece of sugar in the morning."

The door shut, and as Mr. Wisp sat down to make up his list of orders for the following day, the car roared out of the yard with its tired and happy cargo.

CHAPTER EIGHTEEN

THE-DAY-AFTER-TO-MORROW

THE brilliant sun shone in an almost cloudless sky of winter's blue. The air was keen and beautiful to breathe, enlivened by the gentle nip which brought a glow of health and vigorous young life into Jane's face as she arrived with buoyant step on " the-day-after-to-morrow." She was so excited by the thought of riding Peppermint, of controlling that lovely body of life and fire, that she had hardly been able to sleep. She had been unable to concentrate on anything, and had moved restlessly about the house, of course ultimately being ragged by John, who attributed her interest to Peppermint's owner rather than to the horse alone.

" Good-morning, miss," said Irish Jack, emerging from the tack room, tobacco-chewing as usual; " 'tis a glad sight for sore eyes you are this bright and sunny morn, with the little horse all ready and champing in his box."

" Good-morning, Jack," she replied; " do you think he'll be kind with me ? "

" Would he, now ? " he answered; " and would he not be the spalpeen of a horse if he didn't carry ye the living best ? He's a beautiful creature, wid more sense in one eye than many an unfortunate

" He is that, and his strawberry red roan and dark points show off to special vantage this morning. When we canter remember to sit tight, for he may give a playful little buck to start with. Just speak to him and pat his neck. There, see how he crests himself and comes back to you. Steady, Blaze, old boy."

After ten minutes Jane felt thoroughly at home and they trotted on, both horses moving with a long, easy, swinging stride. There was not a soul in sight. They felt as if the earth belonged to them. The weather had been mild of late, and the going was particularly good. They slipped down a steep bank to the sandy track below, which ran for two miles through the hazy blue woods. As Jane put her horse to come down the bank, Carew told her to keep his head straight, to grip tightly with her knees and lean her body slightly forward from the waist, not backward.

" In that way," he said, " you distribute your weight to the best advantage for your horse. In steep countries, such as the Devon and Somerset Staghounds hunt, that's the way you see the huntsman go down a precipitous slope at speed, perhaps for some considerable distance. Have you ever been to that part of the country ?

" No," she said ; " is it very lovely ? "

" It's the most beautiful country in the world. Apart from the staghunting a tremendous amount of riding goes on. You ought to persuade your father to take you there next summer. There is such an air of space and rugged graciousness ; the scene changes from the purple heather of the moors to vast wood-lands filling enormous valleys, and everywhere tumbling down the hills there are little tarns, which unite and open out into shallow rivers, filled with

age-old boulders, worn smooth by time. Amidst such beauty one feels what a mite one really is in the great scheme of things."

"I didn't know you were a philosopher," said Jane.

"Every man who has much to do with horses

becomes a philosopher in time," said Carew. " If
he doesn't, he ceases to be interested. Let's canter
on. Incline his head slightly to the left, and then
use the pressure of your left leg so that he strikes
off on the right leg. That's right. Speak to him.
Whey, my little lad."

Peppermint knew his voice, and cocked one ear
back for it. Jane felt that up till then she hadn't
known what riding was. There was such a length
of rein in front of her, and Peppermint felt so
powerful, yet so smooth, the ground seeming simply
to glide away from under them. Suddenly she felt
his back go taut, then followed a lightning strike-
out of both heels behind, and a duck of the head in
front. Her companion was perfectly calm, but spoke
quickly.

" Grip tight," he said ; " throw your weight on
your knees. Keep your hands low and keep a short
hold of his head."

Three bucks Peppermint gave, but Jane obeyed
instructions to the letter, and still they cantered on.

" That was well done," said Carew. " They
weren't big or vicious bucks, but they'd unship some
people. The great thing is to keep a horse on the
move when he does it ; not to loose his head, and
at the same time to keep your seat slightly off the
saddle, so that as his back comes up it doesn't
contact you enough to pitch you forward. You
don't feel nervous ? "

" Not a bit," smiled Jane. " It was rather fun."
She stole a glance at him, thinking how beauti-

fully and unself-consciously he rode. He seemed so absolutely part of his horse that he could turn his attention to other things. Blaze was cantering on a loose rein, his ears pricked forward and his dark mane tossing backward.

By mutual consent they eased their horses to a walk.

" We've nearly reached the limit of our ride," said Carew. " Would you like to have a jump ? "

" Rather," she replied, " if you think I'll be all right ? "

" I hope so," he answered. " There's a small post and rail fence just over there, with a ditch on the landing side. We'll ride at it at a steady pace, and you'll hardly feel him move. I know he won't turn his head as he'll take it in his stride. Are you ready ? Come on then. Leave it to Peppermint; don't attempt to tell him what to do."

They were about a hundred yards from the obstacle, and as they rode, Carew keeping very close to her, she felt wildly excited. Nearer and nearer it came, until within a very short distance both horses suddenly increased their pace, heads out-stretched and ears well pricked. It came. A pause in the machine-like motion of the muscles, a temporary suspension in the air, a glide downwards and then the slight shock of the earth as they landed.

They were safely over and cantering on again.

" How's that ? " said her guardian.

" Grand, grand!" she exclaimed. " I never knew anything could be so wonderful."

" Gently ease him to a walk," he said. " Now reward him with your voice and hand," patting Blaze himself, " you know more about it, old boy, than I thought you did " ; and again addressing her, " Blaze was inclined to stop, but Peppermint set him such a good example he had to go. A bit different from jumping in the school, eh ? "

" Yes, I should say it is," agreed Jane ; " now I can understand your enthusiasm for racing."

" And hunting," he added. " There's a great joy in negotiating a natural country, where one has to pick one's line. It makes you at one with your horse."

Their heads were turned for home, and as they went Carew explained to her the various points of hounds, hunting, and racing. Being a master of his subjects he made them most interesting and Jane forgot how quickly the time was passing, feeling she could listen to his quiet voice for ever. She was sitting easily when, without warning, Peppermint stood stock-still, planting both front feet and snorting through his nostrils. She urged him on, and up he stood. Up he went, and still up. He seemed to heave beneath her, the earth getting farther and farther away. In time she heard Carew saying :

" Drop your hands, lean forward, sit quiet. Speak to him."

" Heavens, what shall I say ? " she thought wildly, and " Peppermint, Peppermint," came from her nervous lips. His front feet struck once, and after what seemed an eternity he came down.

Carew was at her side, and before the horse could rise again, took hold of the bridle.

" Come on, my lad," he said in an even tone, " what's the matter, eh ? Come along, you rascal."

They went on side by side.

" That wasn't well done," said Jane, " I feel a perfect ass. What made him do it ? "

" Didn't you see that ugly-looking tramp sitting on the ground with his dirty little tent behind him ? Peppermint objected, and I don't blame him. I think you stuck on jolly well, if that's your first experience of rearing ! "

" It is. I felt I should die of fright. You won't tell Mr. Wisp, will you ? "

" Why ever not ? You certainly didn't disgrace yourself."

" I just heard your voice in time, or I should have lost my head and fallen off backwards."

" Peppermint," said Carew, " you're a naughty boy. I hope Jane will forgive you ? "

" Of course I will," she said, patting his neck, and rapidly regaining her confidence as the horse proceeded at his usual free walk, occasionally tossing his head, as much as to say, " What's all the fuss about ? "

The stable gates came in sight. " Oh dear," thought Jane " is my lovely ride over so soon ? "

Carew read her thoughts. " She's a plucked 'un," he thought to himself, " and that little wretch goes well for her too. Does them both good," and aloud, " Well, that's your first ride on Peppermint. But don't think it's your last, because it isn't. We'll fix up another shortly."

" Really," said the delighted girl, " do you mean it ? "

" I do. Hullo, Wisp. Here she is, you see, sound in mind and body."

" Glad of that," said Mr. Wisp, looking keenly at them both.

" Have you enjoyed it, Jane ? "

" Have I not," she answered; " it's been marvellous ! "

" Any trouble at all, James ? "

Mr. Wisp intercepted Jane's little frown of warning to Carew, so he said :

" Ah well, if there was I know she will have weathered it well."

" As a matter of fact, Will, she did," said Carew.

" I knew she would," said Mr. Wisp, as she dismounted, "or I should never have let her run the risk. Don't forget to put the irons up the leathers, Jane."

" There," she said, " I had forgotten. It's the excitement, you know."

" I know," said he. " It must be a wonderful day—the day on which you first ride a high-class blood horse."

" A wonderful day indeed," said Jane.

And as she walked home the words sang in her ears—" A wonderful day and a wonderful horse. A wonderful horse and a wonderful day."

CHAPTER NINETEEN

THE GYMKHANA

THE sleepy village of Feastwell, usually so quiet and deserted that the casual traveller often wondered how on earth it got its name, presented a scene of unwonted activity one hot Saturday in July. The main street with its thatched cottages, here and there broken by a red-bricked Georgian house of long, unrelieved rectangular windows, was alive with inhabitants and visitors from the surrounding country.

Beneath the shade of the "five sisters," five chestnut trees of enormous girth and age, the ice-cream vendors were doing good business, satisfying the greed of children and the needs of adults, who, too numerous for the rustic benches, stood, sat, or reclined on the cooling grass of the village green. Now and then a horseman passed by. Some, peak-capped men with faces of mahogany hue, with a halter beneath the horse's bridle, its rope end neatly coiled in the animal's neck, plainly showing they were on their way to the annual Gymkhana which was to be held that afternoon in a field quite close to the church, of which the Norman tower rose solidly and majestically on a rise at the far end of the village,

178

presiding over it with a conscious air of govern-
ment.

The Gymkhana field itself was the stage of the
liveliest activity. The local bandsmen in their
uniforms of blue, many recruited from the Salvation
Army, blew into their instruments, prepared for
this day to play tunes of gay melody to charm the
ear. Flags on the tents flapped lazily on their masts,
urged thereto by infrequent zephyrs.

Beneath the shade of some trees at the end of
the ground, some fifty or sixty horses were tethered,
their tails whisking away the unwelcome flies. Competitors were standing in groups chatting ; farmers'
sons in breeches and leggings, girls in jodhpurs, one
or two "pot-hunters," hawk-eyed and horsily clad.

Why, there's Mr. Wisp ! Mr. Wisp just the
same as usual, his bowler hat changed to a time-
honoured felt, the welcome brim shading his grey
eyes. There's Jane, and there's John joking with
Peter. Are *they* competing ? They are.

Feastwell, although only fifteen miles from town,
lay somewhat off the beaten track, and had for long
been dear to Mr. Wisp, who loved to return to it
each year on Gymkhana day. In years gone by he
had won many prizes here himself, but was now
content to help his "star pupils" to compete,
and they often benefited by his advice. His enjoyment lay in watching them ride, in seeing their self-
consciousness disappear in the hurly-burly of the
events.

The horses were sent on the day before, the

Lion Inn still retaining its ancient stables, offering hospitality to both man and beast. The church clock struck three-quarters. The loud speaker from the wireless dealer's van, announced in stentorian tones :

" Competitors for Event One, the Open Jumping, please report to Mr. Smith, who is so kindly acting as ringmaster. Every competitor must report to him before entering the ring or will be disqualified."

" That's an improvement," Mr. Wisp said to Jane. " Until this year they have used a megaphone. I took a turn at announcing one day, and nearly lost my voice. Although this is only a village show, they run it well and keep things up to time. That's the way to attract gate money. There's nothing the public hates more than being kept waiting between events. If it happens one year, the next will be a financial failure. Have you got your number ? "

" Yes, thanks ; I'm number twenty-three," she answered, " and John's twenty. Peter has his on already."

" Look," said Peter, and turning round displayed the number fourteen on a white card nearly as big as his back.

" Fourteen's very near to thirteen. I hope you're not superstitious," teased John, who was wearing his jodhpurs on the advice of Mr. Wisp, who said they would not only be easier for quick mounting and dismounting, but less weighty than breeches and boots for his horse to carry.

" A miss is as good as a mile," retorted Peter.

" Anyway I shouldn't care if it were thirteen, and Tinker wouldn't mind either."

Two o'clock struck as the speaker announced the name of the first competitor in the jumping, who was then entering the ring on a thickset brown horse.

The course was arranged round the oval ring, the white wings gleaming in the sun.

" You'll see some good jumping to-day," said Mr. Wisp, " because all the fences have very good wings to them. Good wings of the right height and without gaps are always conducive to good jumping. They keep a horse straight at his fences and take his attention off the crowd."

The attendance was indeed good, and even the keepers of side shows, such as darts and coconut shies had deserted their posts, serene in the knowledge that their turn would come later.

A round of applause greeted the first jumper as he left with " Number two had four faults " from the loud speaker.

" How do they count the faults ? " asked Jane.

" It tells you in the programme," said Mr. Wisp.

" Yes, here it is," said John, reading aloud, " Scale of faults. Horse refusing or bolting, first offence, three faults ; second, six faults ; third, disqualified. Horse hitting obstacle with fore limbs, four faults ; with hind limbs, two faults. Horse and rider fall, six faults. Rider alone falls, disqualified. There are slips on the brush fences, but not on the gate, wall, stile, or triple bar. So now you know."

" Let's see if we can count the faults each time," suggested Peter.

This was their first Gymkhana, and they had been practising for it for weeks. Carew had taught John how to vault on at the canter, trot, and, by far the most difficult feat, at the walk, an achievement in which John had no little pride, and which he hoped he would find useful to-day. Several jumpers had by now been round, the standard of jumping particularly high, as prophesied by their veteran companion.

" Two faults," said Jane, " for number fifteen. Mark that on the programme, Peter."

" I have," said Peter, busy with his pencil.

The next horse was a grey with a sulky eye, and some difficulty arose in inducing him to enter. He finally got going and jumped perfectly. His rider was one of the before-mentioned " horsy gents."

" A real pot-hunter," said Mr. Wisp, " but the horse can jump and the fellow can ride. Well done ! " he exclaimed as the grey cleared the wall in effortless style.

" I don't like the man on him," said Jane, " he has a horrid, cruel face."

" It's a good job the horse can't see it," said Peter.

" Never mind," said Mr. Wisp, " he's going to have a clear round. There, I told you so. Come on, give them a clap. You mustn't be prejudiced by looks, Jane. That horse needed a very experienced man on him."

Several more competed, and then " Last Competitor, number fifty-seven, please," said the announcer.

No one appeared. The grey was the only one with a clear round and looked definitely the winner. " Number fifty-seven ; hurry up, *please*," boomed the voice.

At last a very cocky, brown, short-tailed horse came in, the rider sitting easily, and quite undisturbed by the delay he had caused.

He went at the first fence in great style. Peter turned white with excitement.

"It's Mr. Carew!" he exclaimed. "Look, Jane, it is, it is ! " And then in a slightly aggrieved tone, " He didn't tell me he was coming."

Jane's face also was flushed and excited. She was praying in her mind for a clear round for him, as she watched with what dash and dexterity he cleared fence after fence. The gate, the wall, the double brush in and out, the stile, and a roar went up, as travelling fast at it, they cleared the final triple bar.

" Well done, James," cried Mr. Wisp. " I thought it would be a pleasant surprise for you youngsters ; Mr. Carew has brought the horse all this way from his home specially for you."

" Will they have to jump it off ? " asked Jane. " I do hope. . . ."

She was interrupted by the mysterious voice again.

" Number forty-five and number fifty-seven

each had a clear round. They will jump it off, and the gate and triple bar will be raised four inches. Number forty-five, please."

In came the grey once more, the rider with a more set expression than ever. He cleared the first fence, the second, the third, and "Oh!" murmured the crowd as he just touched the gate with a flip of the hind legs. He finished well without a further fault.

"Number fifty-seven, please."

"Can he do it?" was the anxious thought in four minds. Can he do it indeed! James has no doubt. The horse pricks his ears, the muscles of his neck and powerful quarters shining. Carew sits as still and quiet as a mouse.

"Must be something about that gate," said Mr. Wisp, as the horse showed obvious signs of mistrust as he approached it.

Carew sat down and rode him at it, getting him short by the head and seeming to lift him over.

"That's the way," involuntarily ejaculated Mr. Wisp; "the rest are easy now."

Cheers went up as the course was finished without a fault, Carew patting the horse as he left.

"I guessed he'd win it," said Mr. Wisp, "when he told me he'd entered. He wanted to give you all a surprise, and I think he's done it."

"I should say he has," said Jane. "His name isn't in the programme. So of course we hadn't the faintest idea that he would be here."

"His name's there, right enough; only he's called himself Mr. James."

John looked at his programme.

" I say," he exclaimed, " he's entered in some of the other events ! "

" Of course he is," smiled Mr. Wisp ; " he's going to help you."

The next event was the Novice Jumping, for horses which had never won a first prize. Towards the end of this Mr. Wisp took his pupils over to

the horses to prepare them for their events, carefully checking over stirrup lengths, girths, and so on. Numbers were fastened on with fumbling, nervous fingers, and Peter was in a ferment as he mounted the spicy Tinker for his first event, " Bending Race for Children under Fourteen," for which there were twelve entries to be run in three heats of four.

The fences were just cleared to the centre of the ring when there was a rousing " clear the road " tune on a coaching horn and a red and black coach,

drawn by a well-matched team of bays, **drove into**
the ring. A very smart turnout indeed, the wheels
flashing and the harness jingling, the horses in the
pink of condition pulling like one in the capable
hands of Sir William Thruster, whose teeth held a
long cigar.

"There's a grand sight for you ! " exclaimed
Mr. Wisp. " Sir William handles the ' ribbons ' as
if he were thirty instead of sixty. See his corn-
flower button-hole, Jane ? He'd feel naked without
that. It's sacred to all coaching men."

Right round the ring they drove, the guard
playing " Over the hills and far away," on the " yard
of tin " as the horn is technically termed. A cheer
went up from the crowd.

" Sir William's evidently very popular," said
Jane.

" Rather," said Mr. Wisp ; " he's done that
here every year for the last ten years. The country
people love him. Every day out hunting he has his
pocket filled with sixpences, and never forgets the
man or child who holds open a gate, and always has
a handshake and a minute's chat with any farmer
or gamekeeper."

" Children's Bending Race," boomed the loud
speaker. " Numbers four, five, eight, and eleven
for the first heat."

"Watch this, Peter," said Mr. Wisp, "and you'll
see the value of not going through the last three poles
too quickly so that you overrun and lose ground
turning to go back. Keep cool and leave it to

Tinker, not riding him out until you leave the last post."

The course consisted of ten poles six yards apart with some thirty yards to the starting line. Competitors had to thread these each way without touching, leaving the first pole on the left, and turning at the end.

The first heat was over, won by a girl of ten on a chestnut pony.

"Are you quite ready?" said Mr. Wisp. "Remember what I tell you, and choose one of the inside lines, so that Tinker won't be worried by the crowd."

The band was playing "Chase me, Charlie" as Peter lined up with three other children, choosing an inside course as instructed. Jane and John, now mounted ready for their own bending race, anxiously watched him. Jane was riding the mare Polly, and John, Connie; Mr. Wisp saying one didn't want big horses for this sort of work.

The starter's flag fell.

Peter got well away, Tinker nipping through the posts like an eel, his ears pricked well forward. They reached the end and turned. Three poles to go and Peter lying second, a boy of twelve on a good sort of polo pony leading. It looked certain that he would win, but in his anxiety he caught the last post with his leg and down it fell.

"He's out," said Mr. Wisp. "Keep cool, Peter. Go on, man, ride for it," as a ginger-headed girl came on with a tremendous spurt. Peter did ride for it, shortening his rein and getting Tinker well by the head, almost racing fashion, as Carew had taught them when practising. He crossed the finishing line half a length in front.

"Well done, the young 'un," said a quiet voice behind, as Carew joined them. "He's worth teaching, Wisp."

"He is that," said his friend. They exchanged greetings, a flush of pleasure coming into Jane's face as she said :

"You did jump well."

"I didn't," answered Carew, "but Tom Thumb did."

Peter rode up, his puckish face alight.

"It is hot," he said, failing to look as unconcerned as he desired to appear.

"Put your reins in the right hand," said Mr. Wisp, "keep your foot in the iron and lift your left leg forward on to Tinker's shoulder. Now with your left hand lift the saddle flap and let the girth out two holes. That will let Tinker breathe easier and rest him. He'll need his speed for the final. You won the heat well ! "

"It was lucky that the leading chap knocked his pole down," said Peter to John.

" He was anxious about you," replied John. " You lost some ground on the turn."

" Well, Tinker was pulling my arms out."

" He'll go better next time," said Mr. Wisp. " Keep cool and you may win."

The third heat was run, won by a boy on a grey, who remained in the ring.

" Finalists, please," said the speaker; "numbers five, fourteen, and twenty-six."

There were horses all round them, so Mr. Wisp led Tinker to the entrance. " Best of luck, lad," he said; " use your head and keep cool."

" They're off ! " said Jane. " There's nothing in it, all level. Look at Peter's face ! Good, he's turned shorter this time. Still nothing in it. Now the grey's leading a bit and the girl on the chestnut has lost her cap. They're through," and in her excitement she shouted, " Peter ! come on, Peter ! Oh, what a close finish, I don't know who's won."

It was certainly a close finish, all three together, Tinker and the grey level, with the chestnut a head behind.

" Result of Event Three," boomed the loud speaker whilst the quartette held their breath. Incidentally the voice sounded clearer, its owner having eased his throat with half a pint of beer. " Dead heat for first place between numbers fourteen and twenty-six. Cups will be presented in duplicate. Number five was therefore second."

Peter removed his cap as the judge fastened a red rosette to Tinker's bridle, and rode out of the ring, bashfully but happily smiling, patting the pony's neck, imitating his hero to the life.

It was now John and Jane's turn, but their ponies were not fast enough to compete with some of the cracks kept specially for the purpose and ridden by young fellows who reckon to pay their expenses with their winnings.

They were both naturally disappointed, although Mr. Wisp had warned them that he expected it.

The next event for which they were entered was the relay race, over three flights of sheep hurdles. They knew that pace would also count in this, but Mr. Wisp had entered them to give them confidence. It was arranged that Carew should make the third member of the team and ride his jumper. Both Polly and Connie gave them a good safe ride, but they were outclassed, and finished fourth.

"Anyway," said John, as they rode back to the collecting ground, "we weren't last."

"We're going to win the next one anyway," said Carew. "You'll come in with me, John. The prize is three pounds. If we win that'll be a pound for you, one for Jane, and one for Peter. So we're riding for the Firm!"

They rejoined Mr. Wisp and Peter.

"It's the Pony Express Race," said Peter; "what does that mean?"

"The name comes from the days when in America letters were delivered by hand," said Mr. Wisp. "Before telephones, telegraph, or other mechanical communication. The Pony Express riders were men who rode hundreds of miles at speed, changing their saddles complete with mail bags on to fresh ponies at various stages.

" In this race one man has to ride three times up and down the length of the arena, over three flights of hurdles, using two horses. He rides one horse twice, and one once, having to change his saddle on to each one. What are you going to ride this time, James ? "

" Wait and see," replied Carew. " John's going to be my assistant. Come on, John," and off they went to where Carew's man was standing in a quiet little dell, apart from the bulk of horses.

" Why, that's Peppermint ! " said John.

" It is," replied his companion. " Everything ready, Dickens ? "

" Yes, sir," said the man.

" I'm going to ride Peppermint first and last, and Tom Thumb in the middle. A lot depends on how you help me, John, so pay special attention. This saddle has a girth which clips on instead of buckling as usual. When I come galloping up I want you to stand on the left side of his head with my next horse, facing the way we have to go. I shall be off before my horse has stopped, and whilst I sling the saddle from my horse to yours, you take the horse I've just ridden. In the case of Tom Thumb get out of the way quickly, as when I say 'go,' he'll gallop off, and I shall take a running vault up to save time, as he's not so fast. Is that clear ? "

" Yes," said John.

" Come on then. Dickens will take Connie along to Darby."

This was a popular event, and there were many entries among the keen prize-getters. As they faced the starter the band struck up, " The music goes round and around." Peppermint snorted, tossing his head and pawing the ground impatiently. Carew soothed him with his voice, keeping his eyes glued on the starting flag.

" Are you ready ? Go ! " and the flag fell.

There was a tremendous thunder of galloping horses as they sped away. Carew's racing experience stood him in good stead, and he obtained a lead by the time he reached the second hurdle, Peppermint flying them in his stride. To the keyed-up John it seemed no time before they were back again. Still travelling fast, Carew was off some yards before he reached John and running full pace with his horse. In a trice the saddle was off Peppermint and on Tom Thumb. As the girth was clipped John let go and got out of the way with Peppermint. " Go," said his partner, and as the horse started off he ran, reins in the right hand on the peak of the saddle, left hand holding a saddle flap. He brought both feet together with a spring and swung back and up, and was safely in the saddle before he reached the first hurdle.

John manœuvred Peppermint into position. This time there were three in front level with Tom Thumb. " He'd have been behind but for that method of starting," John just had time to think before changing saddles again. In a flash Carew was mounted and away.

"It's going to be a close thing," said Mr. Wisp, "there are four in the running. James will have to ride Peppermint all out if he's to win."

But James knew what he was doing. He kept the horse well collected with a short rein on the downward journey, so that as he turned round at the bottom he gained two yards from the others who were riding too fast. *Then* he let Peppermint out, and the game beast, responding nobly and even enjoying the fun, began to fly. They crossed the finishing line a length in hand over the second.

Carew returned to John, Peppermint's nostrils flaming. "Nip up on Tom Thumb," said James, "we each get a rosette for this."

A few minutes later they joined the others, leaving the horses in Dickens's hands. The obstacle race was in progress, for which they had not entered. Mr. Wisp describing it as too much of a rough-and-tumble, and anyway, they couldn't ride the same horses in every event.

"It's the tea interval next," said Mr. Wisp. "We'll go to have ours before the tent is too full."

CHAPTER TWENTY

" IF ONLY . . . "

IMMEDIATELY following the tea interval was the Musical Chairs for Children. The Committee were certain of getting the children there for a start to time, whereas they knew from past experience that adults are tardy. It is comparatively simple to run a show well on time up to the interval, but it is sometimes more difficult, although just as necessary, to do the same after. The children's musical chairs served, therefore, as a sort of interim event.

Our friends, thanks to Mr. Wisp's foresight, thoroughly enjoyed their tea in comfort, and were away in plenty of time to get Peter ready for this important attempt to capture another rosette. He had eaten a little lettuce with bread and butter, but they had been unable to persuade him to perform up to his usual standard. His private dread was that he'd get stitch if he ate much, and he was right.

See him now on mouse-coloured Tinker, ready for the fray. He looks very neat in his jodhpurs and white shirt, the sleeves rolled up his undeveloped arms, and his peak cap pulled well down to shade his eyes.

" Two things to remember," said Mr. Wisp. " Keep your pony cantering on the right leg, the off fore, as that's the way you'll go round, and watch the conductor of the band all the time. You'll see him stop the men playing at least a second or two before you can hear the music stop."

The ordinary method of galloping up to a chair, dismounting, and sitting on it, was too dangerous for youngsters, and instead they had to ride into stalls made of sheep hurdles placed in the centre of the arena, there being one stall less each time.

The conductor wiped his moustaches with the back of his hand, tapped his baton on his music stand, and off they went.

It was soon apparent that many of the ponies had never been schooled for it, as although they turned readily enough and galloped to the centre, they showed a mulish reluctance to enter the stalls. This made it easy for Peter to get in, until all the obstinate ones were out, and then the competition became keener.

He had one very narrow shave of being pushed out, and only the fact that Tinker was smaller than his opponent enabled him just to slip in.

" Young Peter's enjoying himself," said Carew.

" Rather ! " said Mr. Wisp. " What fine school-ing for children that is, teaching them how to turn and handle their ponies quickly, and to be sharp about it. As you know, I sometimes have musical chairs in the school at home, using the gramo-phone."

There were now only four left and Peter was still in.

"It would be a good feat if he won it," said Jane. "Just look at the artful imp watching the conductor. He's not paying any attention to his pony."

The band stopped.

"Good," said John, "he's still in."

"Canter on, please," said the judge, arranging them so that the remaining three were equidistant.

The band stopped again and in they went. Peter and the same girl on the chestnut got home, and off they cantered for the last time.

"This is exciting," said Jane; "that's the second time round. There, go on! Go on! Ah!"

The two children had arrived at the stall together, but Peter deliberately let her in. The fast returning audience applauded his chivalrous act, and this time Tinker received a blue rosette.

"Silly ass," said John, "he could have won it. I'm off to mount Connie."

Jane asked Peter why he hadn't attempted to push in.

"She's only a girl," said the little boy, "and I had already beaten her in the bending."

Off went John for the Apple and Bucket race. In this each competitor had to gallop the length of the ground, dismount and, using the teeth only, pick an apple out of a bucket of water, mount, and race back with the apple held in the mouth.

"Any competitor who drops his apple when

mounted," said the loud speaker, " must either dismount and pick it up with his teeth or be eliminated."

A rival competitor had advised John to take off
his collar and tie, and to plunge his head straight
into the bucket without hesitation, thus forcing the
apple to the bottom, when it would be easy to
bite. John followed his advice so successfully,
leaping up as Carew had taught him, that he was
third. He was glad to see that his new acquaintance
was the winner, and went over to congratulate him.

" That's nothing," was the reply, " you'd have
been in the money if you 'd had a faster pony."

The wireless dealer was getting into his stride.
" Will all the ladies and gentlemen get ready for the
Gretna Green Race," he boomed. "Only unmarried
competitors, please, as the Committee have enough
troubles already. Hurry up, please."

" We're in this together," said Jane to John.

" I know," he said with a mischievous look, " but
I don't mind if Mr. Carew takes my place. No fun
for a fellow to take his sister."

" Don't be silly," she answered, but was pleased
nevertheless when James rode up on Peppermint
saying : " Our dance, I think ? "

" Well, it was John's," she demurred.

" I bribed your brother off," he said. " You
know what we have to do ? You race to the far end
of the ground, dismount, seize and read a note you'll
find there. I join you, and you have to tell me to do
what the note says. It may be to give you my tie,
or to kiss you six times, or something like that. We

then mount and race back hand-in-hand. Directly
I've obeyed the instructions face your horse, bend
your left leg, and I'll give you a lift up. But don't
start off without me, because we must be hand-in-
hand. There's only one hurdle to jump."

" Best of luck," said Mr. Wisp, as they rode
off. " Make a nice pair, Darby," as that worthy
stood by him, holding Tinker.

" They do, sir," Darby beamed ; " mayhap them
will someday, sir."

They were second in the first heat, but were
eligible for the final because the first pair were dis-
united for a few yards by jumping the hurdle.
Funnily enough James's suggestion of kissing Jane
six times was what he had to do. Nobody thought
he minded.

" In the final," he said to Jane, " I bet I shan't
get anything so nice to do."

"Don't be silly," she admonished, with the in-
genuousness of seventeen.

In a few minutes their turn came again. This
time Carew had to draw a cow and hand it to the
steward officiating. In this event there was one
steward to every couple. It was a cow that he drew,
just a cow, and that was all, as he admitted afterwards.
Luckily the steward was interested chiefly in pigs,
and not much judge of a cow ! Jane was quickly up
with Carew's help, but Polly was not so fast as
Peppermint, and they were only third. The prize-
getters were mustard !

" These fellows are pretty hot at this game,"

said Carew, as they returned to Mr. Wisp. "They go to a great many shows, and are always practising, besides being well mounted. I anticipated it, that's why I brought Peppermint and Tom Thumb. Does them good to be beaten now and then. But I think you people have done marvellously well in just under a year's riding."

"I think we have too," answered Jane, "when I see all the expert people here, and how they ride as naturally as they walk. It's a tribute to Mr. Wisp's teaching, and also to your kind help."

Two events followed in which they did not participate. The V.C. Race, in which there was a great noise of fireworks and clouds of smoke, as the competitors picked up sacks of straw representing dummy men and raced back, carrying them, over three flights of hurdles ; and the Man and Man Race, which necessitated two men to one horse, each riding and running alternately, and then both riding home bareback on the same horse.

" ' He-men events,' I call those," said John.

" So do I," chimed in Peter. " I tried to lift one of those sacks just now. Gosh, they're heavy."

" The next race will be the last," said Jane, looking at her programme. " It's the musical chairs. We're both in that."

" Well, mind you watch the conductor," said Peter.

" Better still," said Carew, " watch the judge who gives the signal, if you can spot him. It's very difficult to hear the band when you're at the far end

from it. Just listen to the heart they're putting into
' John Peel.' "

Mr. Radio was off again. " Last event of a great
day," he solemnly said, " the Musical Chairs.
Each competitor must dismount and sit on a chair,
not stand on it, as is the reprehensible practice else-
where. I'm looking at you, Mr. Clark and Mr.
Toddy ! Also no person must pull a chair away
from another with his hands. In the ring, please."

Mr. Wisp counted forty-two entries as they
paraded round the ring. He turned to Carew.

"This is going to be hard on the surviving horses,
James. There'll be forty-one gallops and stops. I
don't think our two will stay in very long."

" I know Jane won't," his companion answered.
" She's far too nice a horsewoman to be in that
scramble. But it won't be so bad as that, Will;
they're taking two chairs away at a time."

Their prediction was right, and Jane and John
were soon out. In musical chair competitions there is
sometimes an undesirable practice which unfortun-
ately cannot be stopped. Before the race the experts
agree amongst themselves to mark and to work out
the beginners and amateurs, and leave the real
scrap to come between themselves as time goes on.
And so it was in this competition.

The last two left in were a couple of bold, devil-
may-care fellows. The contested chair was in the
middle of the ring. They were at opposite sides
cantering round, and as the band stopped they
came in at full gallop. Both dismounted and ran

with their horses, and travelling fast they arrived simultaneously at the chair, colliding with a terrific impact. One recovered and sat on the chair. The other was laid out for a minute or two, having lost every ounce of air in his body, but was able to mount and receive his blue rosette. . . .

The band stood to attention and played the National Anthem, which was preceded by a tremendous roll on the drum, given by a little man whose watery eyes turned to heaven and whose walrus moustache fairly quivered with the effort, much to Peter's amusement.

Mr. Radio had his parting shot. "Good-evening, everybody. It's been a most successful day, hasn't it ? Did I hear you say ' Yes ' or didn't I ? Come along, let's *hear* you say ' Yes.' "

The crowd, especially the competitors, responded with a tremendous " Yes ! "

" Then don't forget the dance in the village hall to-night, sharp at 8-30. Mrs. Watkins's prize pumpkin will be on show."

" Rather a wag that fellow," said James to John. " Hope you've enjoyed it ? "

" I should think so," said John enthusiastically. " I'm coming here one day to win, like some of those fellows."

" That's the spirit," said Mr. Wisp.

The horses had already left and they followed suit. Carew packed them all into his car, threading the way through the crowded street for half-a-mile.

In ten minutes they reached the main road and

then he let the car out. The sun was setting in a blaze of splendour, and the pools of green darkness beneath the trees in the fields made a lovely pattern. Mr. Wisp flipped his well-trimmed moustache and sighed contentedly. He was satisfied with the day's work and happy in the knowledge that the successes which were theirs were the result of his own teaching. He loved his work. " Ah," said he to himself, " if only all pupils were as diligent and keen as these, what a nation of horsemen we should be."

INDEX

Figures in italics indicate an illustration.

INDEX

PRINTED IN GREAT BRITAIN AT
THE PRESS OF THE PUBLISHERS

Uniform with this Volume

THE
NELSONIAN LIBRARY

FULLY ILLUSTRATED BOOKS FOR BOYS AND GIRLS
OF ALL AGES AND ALL TASTES

Edited by John Hampden

Uniform with this Volume

THE
NELSONIAN LIBRARY

FULLY ILLUSTRATED BOOKS FOR BOYS AND GIRLS
OF ALL AGES AND ALL TASTES

Edited by John Hampden

24. BARNEY BLUE-EYES. By MABEL MARLOWE.
25. HAUNTERS OF THE SILENCES. By C. G. D. ROBERTS.
26. " WHAT CAN WE DO NOW ? " By RODNEY BENNETT.
27. NEAR EAST ADVENTURE. By Air Commodore L. E. O. CHARLTON, C.B., C.M.G., D.S.O.
28. UNWRITTEN HISTORY. By H. R. HALL.
29. THE BLACKSPIT SMUGGLERS. By LENNOX KERR.
30. RECENT INVENTIONS. By Professor A. M. LOW.
31. ONE HUNDRED BIBLE STORIES. By ROBERT BIRD.
32. A BOOK OF ESCAPES AND HURRIED JOURNEYS. By JOHN BUCHAN.
33. MR. SHERIDAN'S UMBRELLA. By L. A. G. STRONG.
34. SIX IN A FAMILY. By ELEANOR GRAHAM.
35. GREAT FLIGHTS. By C. ST. JOHN SPRIGG.
36. YOUNG ADVENTURERS. By KITTY BARNE (Mrs. ERIC STREATFEILD).
37. KNOW YE NOT AGINCOURT ? By LESLIE BARRINGER.
38. THE MASTER THINKERS. By Prof. R. J. HARVEY-GIBSON.
39. GREAT SCIENTIFIC ACHIEVEMENTS. By Prof. A. M. LOW.
40. THE STORY OF HEATHER. By MAY WYNNE.
41. GALLOPING HOOFS. By JOHN C. DOWNIE.
42. " LET'S GET UP A CONCERT ! " By RODNEY BENNETT and H. S. GORDON.
43. " LET'S LEARN TO FLY ! " By C. ST. JOHN SPRIGG.
44. ADVENTURES UNDER GROUND. By T. C. BRIDGES.
45. " LET'S GO RIDING ! " By B. L. KEARLEY.

Uniform with this Volume

THE STORY OF HEATHER

By MAY WYNNE

Illustrated by Raymond Sheppard

A new edition, with new illustrations, of this established favourite : the fascinating story of an Exmoor pony's exciting adventures.

ADVENTURES UNDER GROUND

By T. C. Bridges

With many illustrations

Great heights and great depths challenge the adventurous, and the depths hold more thrills and secrets than the heights. In this book Mr. T. C. Bridges describes the most daring exploits below ground—in Yorkshire pot holes, Somerset caves, in mines, tunnels, and caverns in all parts of the world. Enthralling stories of disaster and heroism, great engineering feats and miraculous escapes . . . all under ground . . . all true.

Uniform with this Volume

DAILY DANGER

By STUART CHESMORE

With many remarkable photographs

" The daily lives of men who live in the midst of dangers. A series of breathless—sometimes humorous and sometimes moving—escapades."—*Time and Tide.* " Shark fishing, carrying mail by air through any weather and by hand through cannibal infested jungles . . . working on wrecks . . . farming snakes and lions are just a few of the things described."—*The Times of India.*

Uniform with this Volume

THE BLACKSPIT SMUGGLERS

By Lennox Kerr

Illustrated in colour and line by Rowland Hilder

" A most exciting yarn of villainous drug smugglers on the
east coast . . . shots in the night, a chase by a destroyer, and a
wreck at the end—the whole tale admirably told in Mr. Kerr's
vigorous prose."—*John o' London's Weekly.* " Any boy—or
girl—of an adventurous spirit ought to revel in it."—*Time
and Tide.*

213

Uniform with this Volume

" LET'S GET UP A CONCERT ! "

By RODNEY BENNETT and H. S. GORDON

*With a preface by Sir Landon Ronald
Illustrated by Joyce Dennys*

" Every conceivable sort of concert seems to be here—concerts serious and otherwise, concerts for schools, Scouts, Guides, pupils, clubs both musical and social, carol and comedy parties, bazaar musicians, etc. Practical advice to everybody . . . it covers a lot of unexpected but useful topics. There is plenty of humour."—*Musical Times*. " The book should be in the hands of any one who has any share in a concert. . . ."—*Queen*.